Wings of Feathers, Wings of Flame

Books by NORMAN F. SMITH

UPHILL TO MARS, DOWNHILL TO VENUS
The Science and Technology of Space Travel

WINGS OF FEATHERS, WINGS OF FLAME
The Science and Technology of Aviation

Wings of Feathers, Wings of Flame

The Science and Technology of Aviation

---

by Norman F. Smith

Illustrated with photographs
and with drawings and diagrams
by Bill Bradley

Little, Brown and Company
BOSTON TORONTO

LIBRARY OF CONGRESS CATALOG CARD NO. 77–169012

FIRST EDITION

T0 4/72

Published simultaneously in Canada
by Little, Brown & Company (Canada) Limited

PRINTED IN THE UNITED STATES OF AMERICA

To my favorite copilot,
my wife, Lyn

Contents

Introduction

WHEN MAN'S AGE-OLD DREAM of flight was finally realized at Kitty Hawk, North Carolina, near the beginning of this century, hardly anyone noticed. Not until nearly five years later, when the Wright Brothers publically demonstrated their first military airplane at Fort Myer, Virginia, did America and the world suddenly come awake to the possibilities of aviation.

From its frail and uncertain beginning, aviation has moved to a position of dominance in world transportation in less than a man's lifetime. The development of its technology has moved so fast in recent years that it has been difficult even for those who work in this field to keep up. Small wonder, then, that the layman may have been left behind in his understanding and appreciation of the ever-growing wonders of aviation.

From afar, the flying machinery of the aviation world — the airplanes, helicopters, engines, instruments, electronic devices — may seem complex and mysterious. The details of their technology are indeed complex, and often can be understood only by specialists in each particular field. But behind the technology are basic principles that can be understood by everyone.

The wonders of flight can be enjoyed by everyone, whether or not one understands how they are attained. But these wonders may be more meaningful if we understand what is behind them. This book is for the air traveler who is curious about how the chip of aluminum he rides is supported, propelled, and navigated high in the sky; for the fledgling pilot who is seeking an introduction to the skills of flying; and for any reader who is curious about aeronautics and aviation. In this book anyone can ride along as a passenger, or sit up front and take the controls for himself.

Our story will look back briefly at the beginnings of aviation in order to trace the development of some important ideas and achievements, and to fit these into the larger picture of history.

Wings of Feathers,
Wings of Flame

1

Myths, Flights of Fancy, and Serious Work Toward Flight

FLYING WAS EASY a couple of thousand years ago. You needed only to speak a magic word, drink a magic potion, or perhaps imagine yourself strapping a set of wax-and-feather wings to your arms, and the sky was yours. In story, legend, and imagination these devices worked wondrously. But in the real world they didn't work at all, for they were not based upon reality. When we read these ancient myths, we are listening to man's early thoughts and dreams about flight, and watching the efforts he made to figure out how to achieve it. The history of man's efforts to fly show us how his thinking developed through the ages. First he tried to solve the problem with fantasy, magic and legend. Then his imagination led him to the to the trial-and-error method. He built something that he thought might work and tried it. After thousands of years, he began to investigate, to experiment, and solve his problems in a logical way. This approach brought success.

Perhaps the best known of all flying myths is the ancient

Greek story of Daedalus and Icarus, father and son, who built wings of wax and feathers and used them to escape from prison. During the escape flight, Icarus soared so high that the heat from the sun melted the wax. The wings became detached from his arms and he plunged to his death in the sea.

Other legends tell of strange and wonderful flying schemes such as flying dragons, winged horses, winged sandals, flying carpets, and chariots drawn by teams of birds. This last idea of "bird power" is perhaps slightly less absurd than the others — at least birds had shown that they could fly. But here we see what happens when man uses his imagination but forgets to observe the real world. A careful observer might have noticed that no bird can lift much more than himself. He would know that even the fierce eagle seems at times to have trouble lifting some of his smaller victims. We might wonder whether anyone asked himself how many birds would be required to lift a chariot, or thought about how all of them might be trained to pull in the same direction.

Occasionally a glimmer of understanding of the problems of flight appeared in ideas for flying machines. An "aerial boat" proposed in the seventeenth century by an Italian Jesuit named Francesco de Lana, for example, suggested the use of evacuated hollow copper spheres to provide lift (figure 1.1). The inventor seemed to understand that a vehicle lighter than air could fly. But he did not recognize that when he pumped the air out of his copper globes, they would be quickly crushed by atmospheric pressure. His idea was the forerunner of the balloon, which was not invented until a hundred years later. The balloon used a paper or cloth bag instead of a copper sphere, and used hot air or a light gas instead of a vacuum, to achieve lighter-than-air flight.

1.1 De Lana's 1670 proposal for an aerial boat that used evacuated copper balls for lift and a sail for propulsion

Magic potions and magic words were often used in pretensions to flight. During the seventeenth century an Italian monk named Joseph Cupertino became famous for his ability to fly without wings or any other equipment. Many people saw him fly, or so they said, from the rear of the church up over the heads of the congregation to the altar after merely uttering the word *oh!*

In addition to these mythical and imaginary excursions, many men made actual attempts to fly by means of strapped-on wings and batlike garments. These devices were built of lightweight material such as cloth and wood. Sometimes feathers were included, because the builders felt that feathers might possess some helpful lifting power in themselves. Many inventors bravely leaped from buildings and towers to test their designs. Although some may have glided a little, they all made hard landings. As one writer of that time put it, "the weight of his body [had] more power to drag him down than the wings had to sustain him."

That summarized the problem exactly — man was too heavy, and small artificial wings did not produce enough lift. Some who jumped from towers to test their flying devices were killed, but many got off with only broken bones.

It is easy for us now to understand why these "fliers" landed so hard. The answer is available from a simple investigation of almost any bird. If we weigh a bird, and spread out his wings to measure their area, we can obtain an idea of how much wing area it takes to support the bird's weight. The wings of many birds support less than one pound for each square foot of wing area. Some fast-flying, heavier birds, such as ducks and geese, may have wing loadings of about two pounds per square foot. If a 150-pound man were to glide as gently as a bird, he would need about one square foot of wing area for each pound of his weight — or a wing of some 150 square feet in area. A wing this large would be thirty feet long and five feet across! If we consider the weight of the wing itself, a still larger area would be required. We can readily see why the tiny wings that an inventor tied to his arms did not have enough "power to sustain him."

We must remember that the earliest thoughts about flying and the early attempts at flight took place before the days of science — before men began to measure, to investigate with carefully planned experiments, and to figure things out in an orderly fashion. Men of that time were inclined to use their imaginations to design and build something, then try it to see if it worked. When they staked their own lives on the trial, we can only admire their bravery.

Many of the early schemes for flying used man's own muscle power. In those days the only sources of portable power were the muscles of men and animals. No one yet had any inkling that motors would eventually provide the power of dozens, hundreds, and even thousands of horses. The lack of power made the search for a means of flight almost pointless, but this did not deter curious men.

The first important work on the problems of flight came some four or five hundred years ago, when science first began to make significant progress. One of the first serious thinkers about flight was Leonardo da Vinci, who lived from 1452 to 1519. Most famous as an artist, da Vinci was also a musician, architect, mathematician — and perhaps the first aeronautical engineer. He designed a parachute, which he said would permit a man to "throw himself down from any height without sustaining any injury." He designed a model helicopter, which

1.2 Da Vinci's proposed designs for a parachute, a helicopter, and one of his many flapping-wing devices

may have actually flown. Its helical or spiral-shaped rotor was driven by a spring mechanism (figure 1.2). In his thinking about manned flight, da Vinci was influenced by his interest in birds, and spent a great deal of time working on flapping-wing machines. In his sketches he worked out wing structures and flapping mechanisms that were supposed to imitate the wing motions of the bird. These machines, called "ornithhopters," were powered by the arms and legs of the passenger (figure 1.3). Leonardo did not realize that the motions of a bird's wing are much more complicated than he could reproduce with his mechanism. (It is only recently that we have come to understand, through high-speed photography, just how complex these motions really are.) Neither did he realize that the power which a man can produce is very small compared to his weight. No mechanism, however clever, can help him to produce more power. It was not until a hundred and fifty years after da Vinci's time that a biologist named G. A. Borelli came to the conclusion that man's great weight and small power output would make it impossible for him to fly by using his own muscles.

We may think of a bird as a feeble, fluttery sort of thing, but for its size, it is very powerful. With its hollow bones, light weight, and large wing muscles, the bird evolved especially for flight, and is quite different from ground-based creatures like elephants, chipmunks, and men.

If Leonardo da Vinci had worked on the design of fixed-wing gliders instead of bird-like machines, he might have moved aviation — at least the science of gliding — ahead by hundreds of years.

Even after the first glimmer of aeronautical science appeared, men continued to propose nonsensical ways of achieving flight, and to spin fantastic tales of aerial travels. One writer proposed that eggshells filled with dew might produce flight — dew because he had observed that it was "drawn up by the sun," and eggshells because they were light in weight. Other writers suggested magnets or special materials to overcome gravity. The "special materials," of course, were purely imaginary. But along with the nonsense, serious work toward flight continued. Part of this serious work, in spite of its hopelessness, continued to be directed toward flapping machines powered by man's muscles.

But it was not a flapping machine or an airplane of any kind that first lifted man into the air. It was a balloon. In 1782 Joseph Montgolfier in France wondered what it was that made smoke and sparks rise above a fire. If he could capture the "gas," or whatever it was, in a bag, would it have lifting power? He tried it with a small bag made of silk. Much to his surprise, the bag filled with smoke from the fire soared to the

1.3 This model of an ornithopter was built from da Vinci's sketches.
COURTESY OF NATIONAL AIR AND SPACE MUSEUM, SMITHSONIAN INSTITUTION

ceiling of the room. Joseph and his brother Etienne built several larger bags, which they called "aerostatic machines," and filled them with this mysterious "gas." Because they thought that smoke was the mysterious lifting substance, they used a fire of wool and straw which gave off great quantities of noxious smoke. The lifting "gas" was, of course, not smoke but *hot air*. A balloon filled with hot air is lighter than the cold air around it, and rises in the air as a bubble rises in water because it is lighter than the water it displaces. When this principle was understood, balloonists began to use clean, hot fires of charcoal to heat the air in their balloons.

One of the larger balloons built by the Montgolfier brothers soared more than a mile in the air. Soon after this flight, a cage containing a sheep, a rooster, and a duck was sent up in a balloon to find out whether animals could live in the upper air. People at that time knew very little about the earth's atmosphere and feared that the upper air might be poisonous. The story goes that the animals came down safely, except that the sheep stepped on the rooster and injured him. On November 21, 1783, the first manned balloon was launched and carried two men five miles across the city of Paris.

At last man could fly. Not gracefully, like the bird he wished so long to imitate, but instead rather clumsily, swinging in a wicker basket below an enormous bag of hot air.

Balloonists soon found that they couldn't fly where they wanted to — they could only go where the wind happened to take them. But ballooning became a popular new sport.

It was found that a lightweight gas could be used in a balloon instead of hot air. Hydrogen, which was discovered at about that time, is the lightest known gas, and immediately found use in balloons because of its great lifting power. It is extremely flammable, however, and many balloons caught fire accidentally and exploded. In 1785 a hydrogen-filled balloon crossed the English Channel from England to France, carrying two passengers. Armies began to use balloons for aerial observation. Carnivals dropped parachutists from balloons and sold rides to people who wanted the thrill of viewing the earth from a few hundred feet up. Some enthusiasts even talked of flying across the Atlantic Ocean in a balloon, but such a trip was not attempted at that time. In 1897 three explorers left Spitsbergen, Norway, in a huge free balloon in an attempt to fly over the North Pole. The balloon came down halfway to the pole, and all three explorers perished in the arctic cold while making their way back to civilization.

The problem of making a balloon go where the pilot wished it to go was tackled by many balloonists. They tried without much success to propel their craft with paddles, oars, and hand-cranked propellers. Even when the lift was supplied by gas, the thrust that one man could produce with his muscles was not enough to propel a huge gas bag against the wind or even to steer it. About seventy years after the invention of the balloon, a French inventor, Henri Giffard, mounted a small steam engine and propeller on a cigar-shaped balloon and flew the first dirigible airship. The airship was propelled at only five miles per hour by the tiny engine, but it could be controlled and steered.

While the balloonists and dirigible drivers were trying to make practical use of their clumsy craft, other men, who believed that man would some day fly in a *heavier-than-air* machine, were working and experimenting with kites, model gliders, and model airplanes. Later they began to build gliders large enough to carry a man.

One of these experimenters was an Englishman named George Cayley. During the first half of the nineteenth century, Cayley built a whirling-arm device with which he could measure the force on a lifting surface that was moving through the air at various angles. He built and flew model gliders, and developed many new ideas about heavier-than-air flights. He came up with the idea of using a fixed wing for lift and a separate system to produce propulsion — a simple idea to us now, but quite new in those days when the influence of the bird caused most experimenters to try to produce both lift and propulsion by means of flapping wings. Cayley's gliders resembled some of today's model gliders, and had the same arrangement as most of today's airplanes, with a wing up front and a tail behind. Cayley found this arrangement necessary for balance (or what we now call *stability*) in a nose-up, nose-down direction. He also discovered that if the wings extended slightly upward in a shallow V shape, the glider would keep its wings level in flight more readily. This feature, called *dihedral,* is still in use today.

Cayley built larger gliders, one of which lifted a young boy off the ground for a short distance. Perhaps this lucky young man was the first to fly in a heavier-than-air machine. Another of Cayley's gliders lifted his coachman off the ground for a longer flight. The terrified coachman promptly quit, telling his employer that he had been hired to *drive,* not to *fly!*

Cayley realized that the biggest problem in building a flying machine was the lack of an engine with which to propel it. Although steam engines were available, they were much too heavy for flight. A practical gasoline engine which could be used in an airplane was not developed until many years after Cayley's death.

Cayley was in a very real sense ahead of his time. In spite of the fact that he solved many of the problems of flight, he had to be satisfied with flying only models and kites because he had no engine. In one of his papers, he predicted the transport of goods and people "more securely by air than by water, and with a velocity of from 20 to 200 miles per hour." In order to do this, he went on, "it is only necessary to have a first mover [an engine], which will generate more power in a given time, in proportion to its weight, than the animal system of muscles." Cayley's work stands as a monumental achievement in the early science of aeronautics.

Of the many other experimenters who worked on the problems of flight in the last half of the nineteenth century, only a few can be mentioned here. One was Sir Hiram Maxim, an

1.4 The enormous machine built by Sir Hiram Maxim had as much wing area (over 4,000 square feet) as a small transport airplane. An engine of 360 horsepower drove its propeller.

COURTESY OF NATIONAL AIR AND SPACE MUSEUM, SMITHSONIAN INSTITUTION

1.5 Otto Lilienthal gliding over the heads of a crowd

COURTESY OF NATIONAL AIR AND SPACE MUSEUM, SMITHSONIAN INSTITUTION

American inventor who had moved to England. He built a huge machine weighing several tons and powered by a 360-horsepower steam engine (figure 1.4). Its wing area totaled more than 4,000 square feet — more than the wing area of a small transport airplane. The monster craft was mounted on two sets of rails — one to support it, and the other to keep it from rising more than a few inches. On a trial run, the machine lifted off the track. The guard rail failed to hold it, and Maxim had to shut off the steam in order to keep from losing control of his machine. It was damaged when it settled back to earth. Maxim gave up his experiments, and announced that "propulsion and lifting are solved problems; the rest is merely a matter of time." He was right, of course, although one might argue that the birds had already proved that "propulsion and lifting are solved problems." But what Sir Hiram did not attempt to solve was the most difficult problem of all — control of the aircraft in the air.

One experimenter who risked his life — and later lost it — investigating the secrets of controlled flight with gliders was Otto Lilienthal, a German inventor and aeronautical engineer. His gliders had large bird-like wings and a fixed rear stabilizer or tail (figure 1.5). He made more than two thousand flights, experimenting with his method of control, which was accomplished by shifting the weight of the pilot. Lilienthal was the first to demonstrate clearly that controlled heavier-than-air flight was possible for man. In a flight on a gusty day in 1896, Lilienthal crashed and was fatally injured. His death was a shock to the world, and especially to two young men in Ohio who had been following his experiments with interest. They were in the bicycle business, and their names were Wilbur and Orville Wright.

2

The Wright Brothers

SOME SAY THAT a toy helicopter powered by a rubber band inspired the invention of the airplane. Wilbur and Orville Wright were indeed fascinated by this toy which their father had given them. They flew it many times, and even built duplicates when the original wore out, but their strong interest in flying came much later. Their development of the first airplane was probably the product of their inquisitive, pioneering spirit and their deep interest in all kinds of mechanical things. This inquisitiveness was recognized by their father, who encouraged them to pursue their intellectual interests. They read widely, and studied and worked at the things that they enjoyed most. As boys they became interested in making woodcuts, and built a press on which to print them. On this press they began to print a neighborhood newspaper, which proved to be a moderately profitable business. A newspaper empire might one day have been named for them had they expanded this venture.

Instead they became interested in bicycle racing, and in 1892 established the Wright Cycle Company. Building, repairing, and selling bicycles became their daily work, but they continued to pursue other topics which interested them.

The thought of flying really entered their lives a few years after they started the bicycle shop, when they read about the gliding experiments of Otto Lilienthal in Germany. The Wright brothers remained interested in gliding even after Lilienthal's death. They thought of it purely as a sport, but when they began to do some serious reading about the work that had been done on the subject of flight, their interest grew stronger. In 1899, when Orville and Wilbur were thirty-three and thirty-seven years old, respectively, they began serious work on the problems of flight.

Wilbur wrote a letter to the Smithsonian Institution, in which he described his interest in solving the problems of flight and asked for help in obtaining information that had been published on this topic (figure 2.1). He established his approach as that of a scientist and a researcher when he said in this letter: "I am an enthusiast but not a crank in that I have some pet theories as to the proper construction of a flying machine. I wish to avail myself of all that is already known and then if possible add my mite to help out the future worker who will attain final success."

The Wrights also wrote to the author of one of the books they had read, Octave Chanute, asking for information and advice. Chanute, for whom Chanute Air Force Base in Illinois is named, was a successful civil engineer with a great interest in aviation. He had built and flown man-carrying gliders, and was eager to help the Wrights. They became lifelong friends because of their common interest in solving the problems of flight.

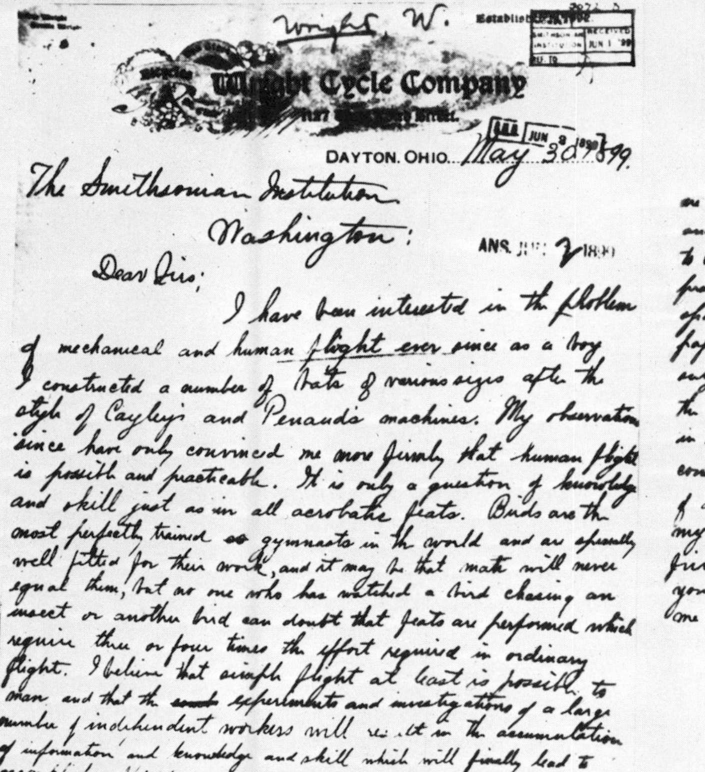

Wright Cycle Company

DAYTON, OHIO. May 30 1899.

The Smithsonian Institution
Washington:

Dear Sirs;

I have been interested in the problem of mechanical and human flight ever since as a boy I constructed a number of bats of various sizes after the style of Cayley's and Penaud's machines. My observations since have only convinced me more firmly that human flight is possible and practicable. It is only a question of knowledge and skill just as in all acrobatic feats. Birds are the most perfectly trained gymnasts in the world and are specially well fitted for their work, and it may be that man will never equal them, but no one who has watched a bird chasing an insect or another bird can doubt that feats are performed which require three or four times the effort required in ordinary flight. I believe that simple flight at least is possible to man and that the experiments and investigations of a large number of independent workers will result in the accumulation of information and knowledge and skill which will finally lead to accomplished flight.

The works on the subject to which I have had access are Marey's and Jamieson's books published by Appletons and various magazine and cyclopaedic articles. I am about to begin a systematic study of the subject in preparation for practical work to which I expect to devote what time I can spare from my regular business. I wish to obtain such papers as the Smithsonian Institution has published on this subject, and if possible a list of other works in print in the English language. I am an enthusiast, but not a crank in the sense that I have some pet theories as to the proper construction of a flying machine. I wish to avail myself of all that is already known and then if possible add my mite to help on the future worker who will attain final success. I do not know the terms on which you send out your publications but if you will inform me of the cost I will remit the price.

Yours truly,
Wilbur Wright.

Wright Cycle Company

DAYTON, OHIO.

2.1 A letter dated May 30, 1899, from Wilbur Wright to the Smithsonian Institution

COURTESY OF NATIONAL AIR AND SPACE MUSEUM, SMITHSONIAN INSTITUTION

In their study of the literature on aviation, the Wrights found that Lilienthal and other gilder pilots had met disaster because they could not control their machines in the air. Gliders of this time were balanced by the pilot shifting his own weight. This method was clumsy and could not be relied upon, as several crashes had proved. The Wrights decided to find a better means of balancing a glider in flight.

Thus, even before they really began work on the problems of flight, the Wright brothers singled out the most important problem which had not yet been solved: how to *balance* and *control* the flying machine in the air. If a gust tipped the machine sideways, a control was needed to raise the low wing. If the machine slipped into a dive or a climb, another control was needed to return the machine to the desired altitude. The success of the Wright brothers in developing the first airplane is due largely to their great wisdom in selecting and solving this all-important problem of control.

They searched for some method of making one wing lift more than the other. They had observed that soaring birds appeared to steady their flight by twisting or warping the tips of their wings. The Wrights hit upon the idea of building two wings held apart by struts so that the whole structure could be twisted like a box with top, bottom, and ends, but no front or back (figure 2.2). By thus twisting or warping the wings, the pilot could increase the lift on one wing and decrease it on the other in order to hold the wings level or to bank the airplane for a turn.

They built a five-foot model of a glider and flew it as a kite. The wings were warped by pulling strings attached to the kite. The model worked so well that they decided to build a full-sized man-carrying glider using the same system of control.

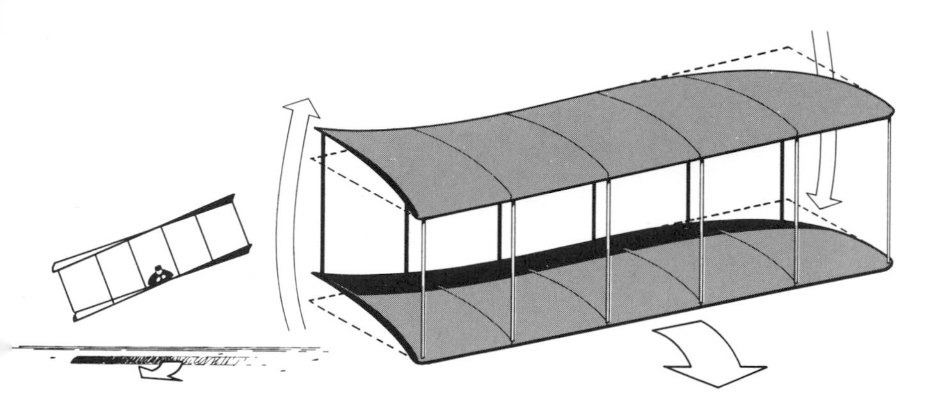

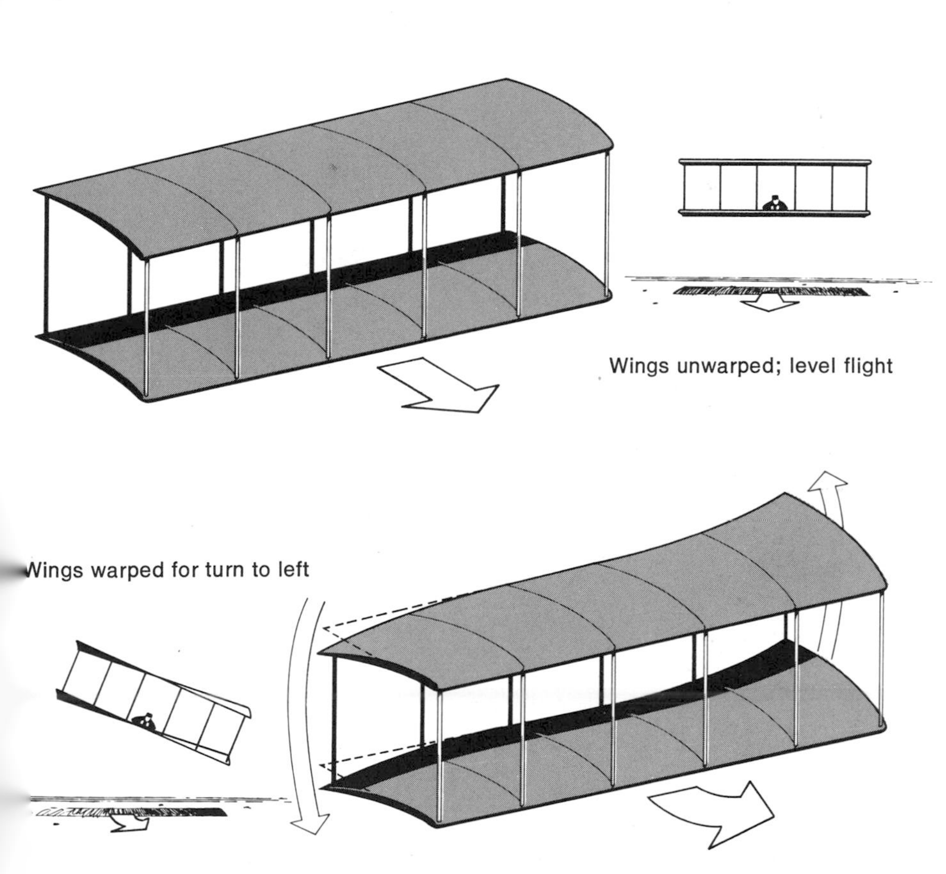

2.2 Warping the wings of the Wright airplane changed the lift on each wing and caused the airplane to roll (bank).

The models and gliders built by the Wrights illustrated another ability that helped carry them to success — their mechanical skill. Many people can imagine, originate, and design, but have little or no mechanical skill for the task of construction. Others who may have the skill to construct cannot design or originate. Because of their rare dual ability to design and to build their aircraft, the Wright Brothers were well qualified for the task they were attempting.

They began the construction of their man-carrying glider, using the materials of the day and the tools and skills learned in their bicycle business. Where should they fly their glider? They needed a steady, strong wind and a large open area. With the help of the United States Weather Bureau, they found that one of the windiest places in the country was Kitty Hawk, North Carolina. With an average wind of sixteen miles per hour, Kitty Hawk often had even stronger winds. The nearby Kill Devil Hill area contained sand hills, or dunes, down which the brothers might launch their gliders, and large flat areas where they could land after flight. With the new glider carefully crated, they traveled from Dayton by train and set up tents at Kill Devil Hill to serve as living quarters during their stay.

The wings of the new glider measured eighteen feet from tip to tip, were five feet wide and were spaced five feet apart. Wings ribs were bent from thin strips of ash wood, and the wing and tail surfaces were covered with cloth. Steel wires tied the wings and struts into a boxlike structure which was strong, yet could be warped in order to produce control. The control cords for the warped action could be operated from the ground or by the pilot. The machine had no rudder. A small horizontal wing which we would call an *elevator* was located about four feet forward of the lower wing. This elevator could be moved by a handle operated by the pilot.

The glider had been designed according to information recorded by Lilienthal, and was expected to need a wind of only sixteen miles per hour in order to lift off with its passenger. The Wrights found that a wind of twenty-five miles per hour was actually needed. They were pleased with the performance of their control system, however, and made a number of flights using the glider as a man-carrying kite. At the end of their kite experiments, they made about a dozen daring free flights, gliding into the air and down the side of one of the dunes with no ropes attached. The machine worked very well, except for the puzzling fact that it did not produce as much lift as was expected.

They decided to check Lilienthal's data on the lifting ability of wings, and built models for making experiments in the open wind. Although their experiments were crude, they seemed to show that the published information on air flow and lift might not be corret. They recorded the results of their experiments for use in future designs.

The next year saw them back at Kill Devil Hill with a new glider, designed according to their new information. This machine was much larger, with a wing span of twenty-two feet. The control cords for warping the wings were connected to a cradle on the wing, in which the operator lay prone. By moving his body from one side to the other, he could operate this control. In experiments with this glider they further increased their growing knowledge of wing lift, balance, and control. But this time the Wrights found that their design information was indeed inadequate. If they were to build a machine that would glide safely, it would be necessary to first obtain better wing-design information.

Back in Dayton, they set up a small wind tunnel to measure forces on wing shapes. The "tunnel" was actually a long rectangular box with a motor-driven propeller at one end to draw a "wind" through the box. By supporting a model wing on a sensitive balance, they could measure the forces on it. With this wind tunnel, the ingenious Wrights began their serious investigation of the effects of airfoil shape (the curvature of the top and bottom surfaces of the wing) on wing lift.

Another new glider was built in 1902, based upon the new wing-design information measured in their wind tunnel. This one was bigger yet — thirty-two feet from tip to tip, with five-foot wings. In addition to the elevator in front, this glider had a fixed vertical fin mounted to the rear to reduce the skidding (sliding sideways) of the earlier gliders (figure 2.3).

This glider proved to be more efficient than earlier models, but it had a new problem created by the vertical fin. When the machine banked slightly because of a gust of air, it began to slide or skid in the direction of the low wing. The wind then caught the vertical tail and turned the airplane in that direction. When the pilot operated his warping control to raise the low wing, the rolling motion of the airplane caused the nose to swing still further in the direction of the low wing. The Wrights called this wild maneuver a "tailspin," although it was not the same maneuver that is called a spin today. This problem gave their glider a wallowing motion as it skidded from one side to the other in bumpy air, and several times the glider struck the ground with its low wing, thereby ending

2.3 In 1902 the third Wright glider sails down a dune at Kitty Hawk with Wilbur at the controls.
COURTESY OF NATIONAL AIR AND SPACE MUSEUM, SMITHSONIAN INSTITUTION

the flight. The problem was soon solved — the fixed vertical fin was made into a *movable rudder* and connected to the wing-warping controls. With this arrangement, warping the wing to roll the airplane also deflected the rudder to keep the airplane pointed straight ahead while it was rolling to a banked altitude. (The rudder is used by pilots today in exactly the same way, as we shall see in a later chapter.) With this new control, hundreds of successful gliding flights were made.

Feeling that they had solved the problems of balance and control, Wilbur and Orville began to think of building a new machine with an engine. They had an advantage over Cayley and all the other experimenters who came before them: the gasoline engine had been invented, and had been in use for several years in those crude buggy-like vehicles known as automobiles. The early engines were heavy and not very powerful, but they were far superior to the steam engine.

In their methodical way, the Wrights calculated how much power their proposed airplane needed and how much the engine could weigh. When they wrote to the best-known manufacturers of automobiles and asked whether the engine they needed could be supplied, they received no favorable answers. No one was interested in attempting to build the small lightweight motor they needed. Perhaps no one thought it could be done. Undaunted, the Wrights designed a motor of their own, hoping for about 8 horsepower and a weight of less than 180 pounds. The engine they built proved to be more powerful than they had hoped — it produced a little over 12 horsepower. It was heavy — over 160 pounds — and it was clear that an airplane larger than their latest glider would be needed to carry it.

The new machine was 40½ feet tip to tip, and looked very

much like the previous glider. The propeller presented a problem. Propellers had been used on ships for many years, but they were small in diameter and quite different from those needed for use in the air. Information on how to design propellers was almost unknown. The Wright Brothers studied the problem and designed a pair of propellers which they carved in their own shop. Slowly the new machine began to take shape, and in November, 1903, it was shipped to Kitty Hawk for assembly at the test site.

While the Wrights were drawing closer to their historic day, other workers were making progress with their projects, Samuel P. Langley, an American scientist, seemed to be well ahead in the race to fly. Langley had been working on the problem of flight since 1886. For about five years he experimented with rubber-band–powered models, then began to look for a more practical source of power. He tried steam engines, then compressed-air engines, but had great difficulty in building a model that was strong enough to carry an engine, yet light enough to fly. In 1893, from a platform built on a scow anchored in the Potomac River, he began launching models powered by steam engines. All were failures for one reason or another, until 1896, when one of his models made a flight of about a minute and a half. This was probably the first sustained flight of a powered heavier-than-air machine. After two more successful model flights, Langley stopped his experiments. He had proved that powered heavier-than-air flight was possible, and was willing to leave to others the commercial and practical development of the idea. Langley was then sixty-three years old, and wished to devote his time and energies to his tasks as secretary of the Smithsonian Institution, a post which he had held since 1887.

But President McKinley had other ideas. He had read a magazine article in which Langley predicted the use of the flying machine for war purposes. The President was then busy with the war between the United States and Spain, and began to think of the possibility of using the airplane as a weapon of war. He offered Langley the opportunity to continue his aeronautical work on a $50,000 War Department grant, with a man-carrying airplane as his goal. Langley was reluctant, partly for reasons of health and age, but finally agreed to continue with the project, giving his personal services to the government without charge.

Because Langley was unable to procure a lightweight engine for his project, his assistant, Charles M. Manley, designed an engine and built it in the Smithsonian shops. His first engine developed 18½ horsepower and weighed 108 pounds. He then designed and built another engine large enough to power the huge flying machine Langley had planned. It was an amazing engine for its time, producing 52 horsepower and weighing only 124 pounds.

Langley insisted that the man-carrying "Aerodrome," as he called it, be a large copy of the smaller models that had made successful flights a few years earlier. He also decided, against his assistant's wishes, that it, too, should be launched from a houseboat or barge on the Potomac River. Not wishing to risk a man's life in the attempt, he planned to launch the first Aerodrome with ballast in place of a man. Manley persuaded Langley that chances of success would be greater if he were aboard as a pilot, and a pilot's compartment for young Manley was installed along with a control wheel. The wheel only controlled the up-and-down motion of the tail of the craft; the Aerodrome had no lateral (banking) control.

Several more launchings of models were made from the barge, to check the launching apparatus and to gain more experience. One of these models was powered by a small gasoline engine built by Manley and his team. Its flight was another first for Langley — the first gasoline-powered heavier-than-air model ever to fly.

Delays and problems, some of which were due to extreme dampness aboard the barge, plagued the project, but on October 7, 1903, the full-sized Aerodrome was assembled and ready on its huge platform sixty feet above the Potomac River (figure 2.4). The engine was started, and the twin propellers whirled smoothly as the machine, with pilot Manley in the cockpit, tugged against its restraining cable. At a signal from Manley, the cable was cut with an ax. The 850-pound machine shot across the launch platform toward the edge. Free in the air, the Aerodrome immediately nosed downward toward the water (figure 2.5). The pilot turned the control wheel to bring the nose up, but the vehicle did not respond. Its dive steepened, and it plunged nose first into the water below. Manley found himself underwater, but struggled free of the wreckage and swam to the surface.

Langley issued a statement saying that the Aerodrome had snagged the launching gear and had not been launched properly. Because the engine had not been damaged by its dunking in the river, and because many spare parts for the Aerodrome were already available, Langley promised that another flight could be made in about a month.

On December 8, the vehicle and its crew were again ready. It was late afternoon on this gusty winter day when the restraining cable was again cut and the Aerodrome sped down the catapult track once more. This time the craft pitched up as

2.4 The Langley Aerodrome poised on top of its launching barge in the Potomac River

COURTESY OF NATIONAL AIR AND SPACE MUSEUM, SMITHSONIAN INSTITUTION

2.5 Launched from the barge, the Langley Aerodrome plunges toward the water.
COURTESY OF NATIONAL AIR AND SPACE MUSEUM, SMITHSONIAN INSTITUTION

it vaulted into the air. Manley again whirled the control wheel to bring the aircraft to level flight, again with no effect whatever. The Aerodrome whipped up into a vertical attitude, its tail and rear wing in shreds, its front wing crumpled, and settled backward into the cold water below. Manley managed once more to tear himself free of the wreckage, came up under a block of ice, and had to dive again to come up in open water.

The cause of this second disaster is unknown. The tail may have again fouled the launch mechanism, the strains of launch in gusty air may have induced structural failure, or the structure may simply have been too frail to begin with. As the Aerodrome vanished beneath the waves in the gloomy December twilight, Langley's last chance to accomplish the first manned flight also vanished. The money provided by the government was gone, the war with Spain was over. There would not be another attempt.

Langley's achievements had been considerable. In his model tests he had developed a very "stable" airplane — one that would "fly itself" for a fairly long distance. He had flown the first sustained heavier-than-air model flight, and the first gasoline-powered model. But in spite of his successes with models, he had not solved the problems of control, pilot skill, and others that seemed to be required for successful flight of a man-carrying machine.

When the Wrights started the engine of their machine on December 14, 1903, they were ready. In their methodical, step-by-step process, they had explored the principles of lift and control in their wind-tunnel and glider work, and had proved their designs in hundreds of actual glider flights. They had taught themselves to fly and had spent enough time in the air to become highly skilled pilots. Although the step they were about to take was a large one, it had been reduced to reasonable size by their careful preparations.

Wilbur was at the controls for the first attempt, but through an error in handling at the start, the machine was slightly damaged. Repairs were readily accomplished, and on December 17 the craft was again mounted on its launch track, pointed into a brisk 20-mph wind. With Orville at the controls and the two propellers whirring smoothly, the machine rose from the track and covered 100 feet in about 12 seconds (figure 2.6). The next two flights were nearly twice as long, and on the fourth flight the airplane flew for 59 seconds and covered 852 feet. While the machine sat on the ground waiting for another flight, a gust of wind upset it and turned it over and over, damaging it severely. This airplane was never flown again. It now hangs in the National Air and Space Museum of the Smithsonian Institution (figure 2.7).

Orville Wright sent a historic telegram to his father in Dayton:

SUCCESS FOUR FLIGHTS THURSDAY MORNING ALL AGAINST 21 MILE WIND STARTED FROM LEVEL WITH ENGINE POWER ALONE AVERAGE SPEED THROUGH AIR THIRTY-ONE MILES LONGEST 59 SECONDS INFORM PRESS HOME CHRISTMAS

ORVILLE WRIGHT

When Orville sent the words "inform press," he probably didn't expect the story of the first flight to explode onto the front page of every paper in the country. The Wrights were not greatly secretive, nor were they publicity seekers. But they could not have guessed the public reaction — or more accurately lack of reaction — that was to occur. The story

2.6 The Wright *Flyer* leaves its launch track to make the first successful manned airplane flight in history on December 17, 1903. Orville Wright is at the controls and Wilbur is standing at the right. COURTESY OF NATIONAL AIR AND SPACE MUSEUM, SMITHSONIAN INSTITUTION

contained in Orville's telegram was delivered to the editor of the Dayton *Journal*. His gruff response was "Fifty-seven* seconds, hey? If it had been fifty-seven minutes then it might have been a news item." Nothing appeared in the paper that day.

A garbled version of the telegram came to the editor of the Norfolk *Virginian Pilot*, who printed it and offered the story to twenty-one other newspapers. Five asked for the story, but

* *An error in transmission of the telegram had changed "59" to "57."*

only one, the Cincinnati *Enquirer,* printed it. A highly inaccurate story appeared in many newspapers a few days later reporting a three-mile flight by a machine that employed two six-bladed propellers, one for lift and one for propulsion.

People who heard of the flight seemed not to be impressed. They had heard of dirigible flights in Europe by Santos-Dumont and were unable to see anything new in the Kitty Hawk flights. Others had been influenced by the many distinguished scientists and experts who had declared in speeches and articles that heavier-than-air flight was impossible, absurd, and not to be expected, ever. And then there were Langley's ill-fated flights of a few days before, which had received considerable publicity and had seemed to prove that the skeptics were right — flying *was* impossible.

Aside from a few garbled newspaper accounts and a few magazine articles the following spring, the Wrights received little publicity. They began to think about developing the airplane further, and set out in 1904 to build a new machine. It was almost exactly like the 1903 machine, but heavier and stronger, and had a new 16-horsepower motor.

They decided to fly the machine at a field outside Dayton, and invited reporters from Dayton and Cincinnati to witness their first flight. About a dozen newspapermen came, along with two dozen other invited people. The wind was uncooperative, changing from too much to too little, and forced cancellation of the flight. In order not to disappoint the visitors, the Wrights started the engine to show how the launching track worked, but the engine balked and ran very poorly. They invited the visitors to return the next day, but only two or three of the newsmen showed up. The engine was still running poorly, and the machine flew for only sixty feet. The reporters

2.7 The construction details of the Wright 1903 airplane can be seen in this photograph taken in the Smithsonian National Air and Space Museum. COURTESY OF NATIONAL AIR AND SPACE MUSEUM, SMITHSONIAN INSTITUTION

were unimpressed, but wrote friendly articles about the flight. None of them ever returned to the flying field again.

The Wrights made or attempted 105 flights during 1904, the longest of which was five minutes and included more than three complete circles of the field. In 1905 another new machine was built with which they began to make longer flights, finally reaching a distance of twenty-four miles in thirty-eight minutes.

During all this activity, held within sight of the interurban rail line to Dayton, reporters paid no attention to the Wrights and little or nothing appeared in the newspapers in Dayton or elsewhere. Even when people who had seen flights from the interurban cars called the newspaper to ask why they had not been reported, the newspapers failed to investigate. It was not until 1906, nearly three years after the first Kitty Hawk flights, that important articles began to appear telling of the Wrights' achievements.

When the Wrights attempted in 1905 to offer their invention to the United States government, the response they received was almost unbelievable. They wrote to their congressman, describing their flights thus far, and asked whether the government was interested either in purchasing flying machines or in acquiring the information they had accumulated. Their letter was sent to the War Department, which evidently didn't believe their story.

". . . the Board has found it necessary," ran the reply, "to decline to make allotments for the experimental development of devices for mechanical flight, and has determined that before suggestions with that object in view will be considered, the device must have been brought to the stage of practical operation without expense to the United States. It appears from the letter of Messrs. Wilbur and Orville Wright that their machine has not yet been brought to the stage of practical operation, but as soon as it shall have been perfected, this Board would be pleased to receive further representations from them in regard to it."

Although the Wrights had clearly stated in their letter that they had developed their machine "to the stage of practical operation," the War Department chose to ignore their claim. The Wrights began to negotiate with the British government for a contract to build an airplane for Britain. Later they wrote another letter to the Secretary of War of the United States, again offering to build an airplane for the United States government. The War Department once more stated the government's position that no allotment of funds would be considered until "the device must have been brought to the stage of practical operation without expense to the government." The letter further stated that the Wrights must furnish "such drawings and descriptions . . . as are necessary to enable its construction to be understood and a definite conclusion as to its practicability to be arrived at."

The Wrights patiently wrote again, offering to build an airplane for the United States government if the government would tell them what conditions and performance were desired. The answer to this letter reflected the War Department's apparent inability to believe or grasp what the Wrights had already accomplished: "The Board does not care to formulate any requirements for the performance of a flying machine or take any further action on the subject until a machine is produced which by actual operation is shown to be able to produce horizontal flight and to carry an operator."

The goal of human flight, so long sought by so many people,

so beautifully accomplished by the genius of the Wright Brothers, had not been greeted by loud acclaim but by a quiet yawn. The general population, and the government itself, was so steeped in disbelief and apathy that three more years were to pass before the nation began to grasp the fact that two Americans had really flown — not just once, but more than a hundred times.

President Theodore Roosevelt set the machinery in motion that was to bring the indifference of both the public and the government to an end. After Roosevelt's attention was called to an article on the Wrights in the *Scientific American,* his administration took steps to invite the Wrights to make a proposal for supplying an airplane to the government. Late in 1907 the agreement was completed. The specifications stated that the airplane must carry two people, including the pilot, be able to fly for one hour, show an average speed of 40 miles per hour, and carry enough fuel for a 125-mile flight. Though these requirements may have seemed impossible at the time, most of them had already been attained or were within easy reach of the Wrights. The price of the airplane was set at $25,000 with a 10 percent bonus for each mile per hour over 40 and a 10 percent penalty for each mile per hour under 40.

The first demonstration flight of the military airplane in history took place at Fort Myer, Virginia, on September 3, 1908. Orville Wright flew for just over a minute before a crowd of hundreds of people, and on landing was quickly surrounded by a crowd of excited, enthusiastic newsmen. The public was awake now. Orville lengthened his flights steadily until he was remaining aloft for more than an hour, and easily fulfilled all the requirements for the demonstration flights.

On September 17, tragedy struck. Lt. Thomas Selfridge, a

young West Point–trained army officer, was a passenger in the demonstration airplane when a stay broke, causing the airplane to go into a near-vertical dive. Orville almost succeeded in righting the airplane, but the resulting crash demolished the airplane and injured both pilot and passenger. Selfridge died of his injuries, the first person to be killed in an airplane accident. Orville had a broken leg and some broken ribs, but recovered to fly again.

The accident did more than anything else had done to carry the airplane into the news. Widespread incredulity finally ceased, and long-overdue credit and acclaim began to come to the Wright Brothers.

In 1935, a memorial was erected on a tall sand dune near Kitty Hawk, one of the largest monuments ever erected in honor of a living American.* You can drop in if you're flying that way, and land beside the dune on the smooth, paved airstrip appropriately named First Flight. Two gray, weather-beaten sheds beckon in the distance — replicas of the hangar and living quarters erected here by the Wrights. The dunes are not naked, shifting sand any more (they have been stabilized with a cover of grass and shrubs), but the wind still rushes in off the ocean, and the wide open spaces are still there, preserved now as a National Park. Near the hangar, a short steel launching track and a stone tablet tell us that this is the spot. . . .

In the museum nearby hangs a replica of one of the Wright gliders, a frail ancestor of the sturdy wings that bring thousands of people to the airstrip each year.

It would be difficult for anyone to land at First Flight airstrip without feeling the strong presence of history. On depar-

** Only Orville was still living. Wilbur Wright died in 1912.*

ture, a silent dip of the wings might be appropriate, to honor the extraordinary human achievement that took place near those tiny gray buildings among the dunes far below.

3

Pushing the Air Around

THE MODERN AIRPLANE is so sleek and streamlined that we might suppose it is intended to fly without disturbing the air at all. Nothing could be further from the truth. If the airplane did not disturb the air in very special ways it simply could not fly.

A balloon can hover quietly, with no disturbance, moving only when the wind moves, because it is light enough to float in the air. But an airplane is much heavier than the air around it and cannot float. Instead it must *do* something to the air to make the air support its great weight.

What must it do? How is lift produced? This is the problem that stumped man for so many centuries and even today is sometimes not clearly understood. The bird gives us a hint by flapping its wings. But alas, air is invisible, so we cannot really tell by observation what happens to the air as it moves around a bird's wing. Watching an airplane doesn't help much, either — it slips through the invisible air without seeming to do anything.

But the helicopter, which was developed some years after the airplane, reveals the secret if we look closely. If you have ever stood near a helicopter as it left the ground, you know what a commotion the helicopter rotor produces. The rotor spins faster and faster when the pilot is ready to take off. Dust and leaves that begin to fly out from under the machine show us that the rotor is *directing air downward.* When the downward blast of air is strong enough, the helicopter leaves the ground.

Sir Isaac Newton, who is best known for telling us about the law of gravitation, stated in 1700 the law of mechanics which the helicopter illustrates:

For every action there is an equal and opposite reaction.

This short statement, known as Newton's third law, tells us how lift and propulsion of airplanes is produced, and applies as well to many other everyday experiences. This law applies whenever two things act upon each other. Its application to the helicopter is quite simple. The two things acting upon each other are the *air* and the *blades* of the rotor. If we want the air to produce a lifting force on the rotor, we must, according to Newton's law, make the rotor produce an equal and opposite effect upon the air. If the lift force on the rotor is to be *upward,* the force exerted on the air must be *downward.* So the helicopter rotor as it spins faster and faster directs a stronger and stronger blast of air downward. When the downward push on the air produces an upward force on the rotor that is greater than the weight of the helicopter, the vehicle leaves the ground (figure 3.1).

3.1 Newton's third law requires an action (downward acceleration of air) to produce a reaction (lift) for both helicopter rotor and airplane wing.

It is interesting to note that until a few hundred years ago air was considered a very mysterious substance. No one knew what air was made of or even understood that air was a material substance. Two students of Galileo, Torricelli and Viviani were perhaps the first to realize, through their experiments with the barometer over three hundred years ago, that air has mass, or weight. Of course we know now that if air had no weight, it could not exert a force on us as we walk in a strong wind; the hurricane and the tornado could do no damage to trees and houses; and no bird, airplane, or balloon could fly. And no matter how fast a helicopter rotor spun, no lift would be produced.

The airplane wing produces lift by exactly the same principle as the helicopter, though it does it in a little different way. It may simplify our examination of the process if we consider the wing to be stationary with the air flowing past it — the effect is exactly the same as when the wing moves through still air. If air approaches the wing horizontally, flows over its upper and lower surfaces and departs in a horizontal direction, no lift is produced. The wing must be tilted with respect to the oncoming air to deflect the air downward if lift is to be produced.*

The angle at which the wing meets the oncoming air is called the *angle of attack.* Watch an airplane roaring along the

* *The principle of lift in many primary and secondary textbooks and in some popular literature is not so simply stated, but has become confused by discussions of velocities, pressures, and the "Bernoulli principle." This confusion is unfortunate and unnecessary. There can be no lift unless Newton's third law is satisfied. The force on all lifting surfaces is due* entirely *to downward acceleration of air. Bernoulli's theorem is concerned only with the relationship between pressures and velocities, and does not in any way explain the* source *of lift, regardless of the many and varied attempts to use it thus.*

runway for takeoff and you will see that the airplane does not leave the ground until the pilot raises the nose to increase the angle of the wing with respect to the oncoming air. When the airplane wing deflects enough air downward, the airplane leaves the ground and climbs into the sky.

Air is light in weight — how does the wing get hold of enough air to produce the huge force needed to lift an airplane? The answer is that the wing affects the air at a great distance above and below the airplane. Picture a huge circular pipe of air with the airplane flying down the middle, its wing tips almost touching the wall of the tube, and you have roughly the amount of air that the wing deflects. The smoke-tunnel picture (figure 3.2) shows how the air flows over a wing. The white

3.2 Filaments of smoke make airflow visible in this wind-tunnel photograph. COURTESY OF NASA

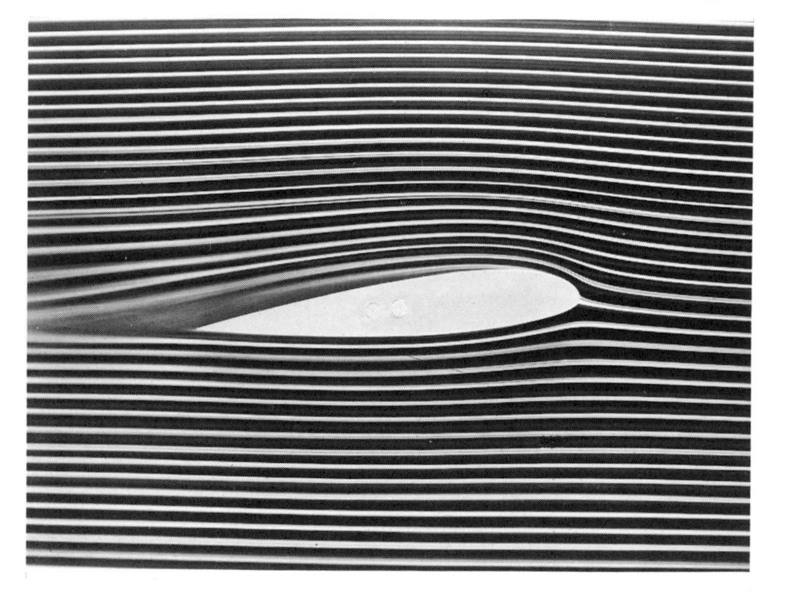

object is the *airfoil* (the endwise view of a wing) and the white lines are filaments of smoke in the airstream. From the bending of the streaks of smoke, we can see that the flow field all the way to the top and bottom of the picture — and probably beyond — is being affected by the wing. Unfortunately, both the wind tunnel and the fuzzy smoke filaments are too crude to show accurately the difference in the angle of flow ahead and behind the airfoil. But we know that between the undisturbed region ahead of the airfoil and the region behind the airfoil, a downward deflection takes place if the wing is producing a lift force.

Looking a little more closely at what happens on the surface of the airfoil, we find that the only way air can exert a force on a solid body, such as a wing, is through *pressures*. We can feel the force of air pressure on our hand if we hold it outside the window of a moving car. As the air moves over the wing (and all other parts) of the airplane its pressure and velocity change from place to place. For example, there are "negative" pressures (less than atmospheric) pulling on the wing in some places and "positive" pressure (greater than atmospheric) pushing on the wing in other places. Figure 3.3 shows how these pressures might act on an airfoil; the amount and direction of the pressures are indicated by the arrows. These pressures always balance each other (or "add up to zero") and produce no lift on the wing if the wing is deflecting no air downward. When the wing is tilted to an angle of attack the pressures change so that they no longer cancel each other. As the bottom sketch shows, the pressures on top then become more negative and the pressures on the bottom become more positive, and an upward lift force results. It makes no difference whether the airfoil is flat on both sides, flat on one side,

If symmetrical airfoil has no angle of attack, pressures balance and no lift is produced

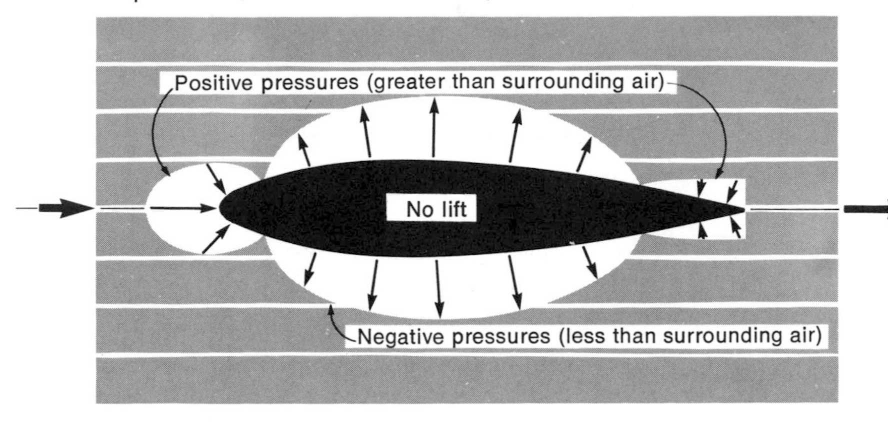

If airfoil has an angle of attack, air is accelerated downward; pressures change to produce a lift force upward

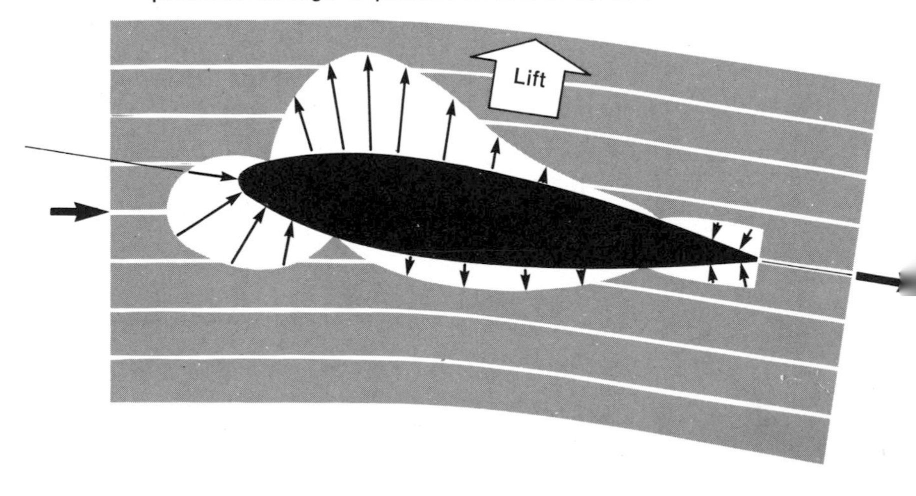

3.3 Pressures generated by air motion do not add up to produce a lift force unless the airfoil acts on the air to accelerate it downward.

or the same shape on both sides (symmetrical) like the one in the sketch. The vital point is that the pressures will always add up to zero lift unless the airfoil is deflecting air downward. Newton's law, remember, requires the wing to act upon the air if the air is to react upon the wing.

Another of Newton's laws helps us to understand just *how much* air deflection is needed to lift an airplane. The force produced, says Newton's second law of motion, will be equal to the mass of air deflected multiplied by the acceleration given to it. This is simply Newton's famous equation:

$$F = ma$$

When we are talking about wing lift, we can write this expression as:

$$\text{Lift} = m \times \Delta\, v$$

where m is the amount (mass) of air deflected by the wing per second and Δv* is the change in velocity (acceleration) given to that air. We need not be concerned with the mathematics of this equation, but from it we can learn one of the most important things we need to know in flying: the way in which lift, speed and angle of attack are related. The lift we need can be produced by multiplying a *large* mass of air by a *small* change in velocity *or* by multiplying a *small* mass of air by a *large* change in velocity. The first condition in figure 3.4 corresponds to high speed, where the wing affects a large amount of air and needs only a small angle of attack to deflect this air a small amount. The second condition in figure 3.4 corresponds to low

* *Δ is the Greek letter "delta," used here to mean "change."*

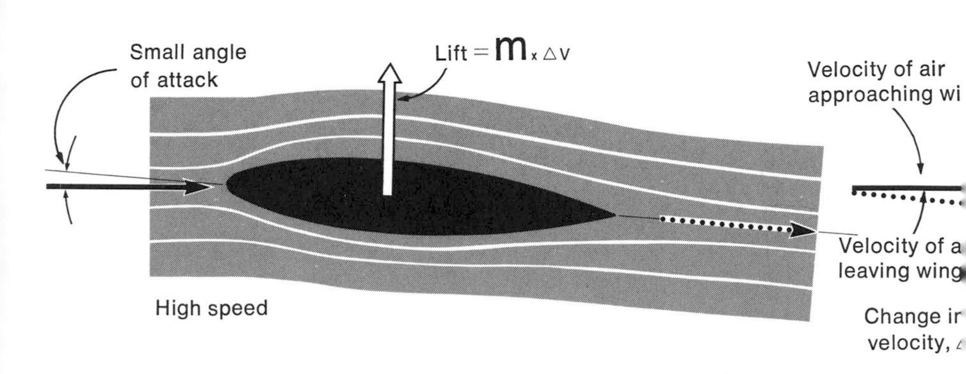

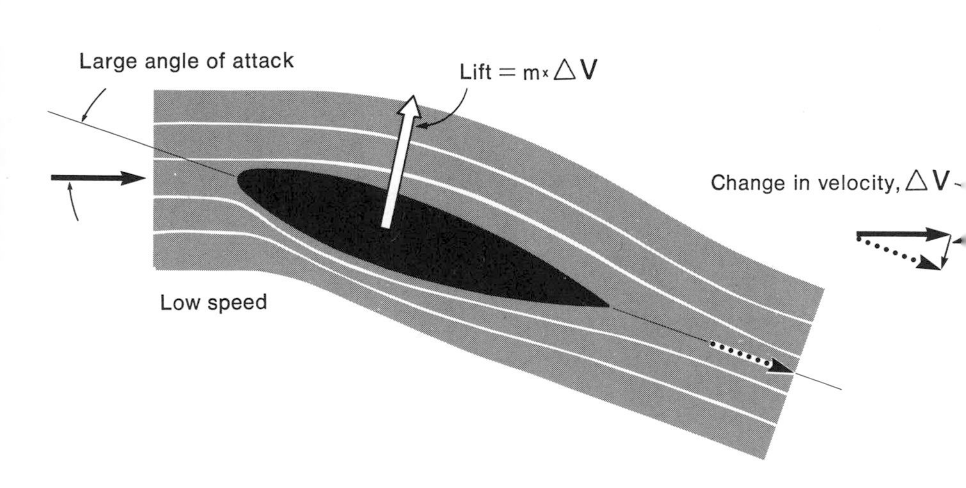

3.4 Newton's second law ($F = ma$) explains how lift, speed, and angle of attack are related. The same lift can be produced by giving a large amount of air a small deflection (change in velocity) or a small amount of air a large deflection.

speed, where the wing affects a smaller amount of air and needs a larger angle of attack to deflect this air a large amount. Thus, we can fly an airplane at many different speeds, but its angle of attack for any speed must produce adequate deflection of air if enough lift is to be maintained.

If we try to fly at too low a speed, the airplane's angle of attack will become so large that the air can no longer follow the sharp turn over the top of the airfoil. Instead, it will tear away from the surface and swirl back in rough, turbulent flow (figure 3.5). The wing is said to be *stalled*. Because the wing is deflecting less air downward, the lift decreases sharply. The lowest speed at which we can fly an airplane is thus called the *stalling speed*.

3.5 When stall occurs, the flow separates from the upper surface of the wing and the lift decreases.

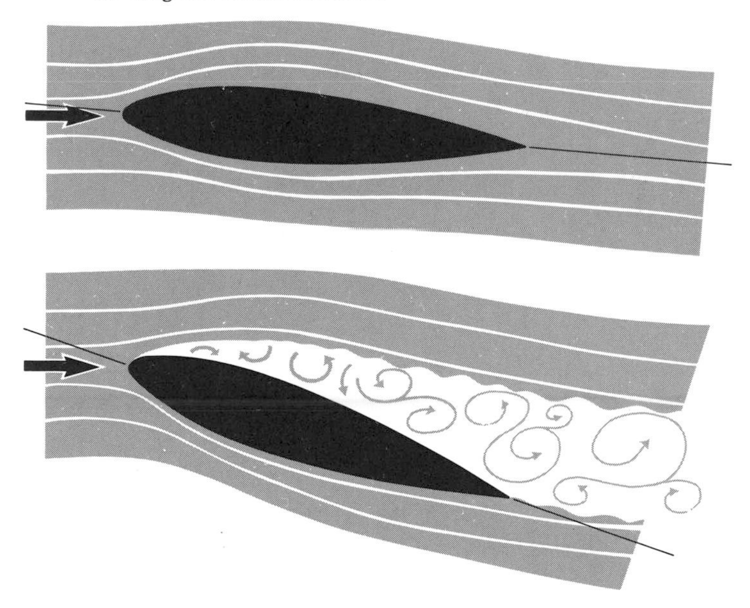

Although lift is the number one requirement for flight, it is by no means the only one. Two other requirements are *stability* and *control.* To answer these needs the airplane is provided with many fixed and movable surfaces (figure 3.6). By the term "stability" we mean the ability of the airplane to return to its original condition of flight after it has been disturbed. A ball in a bowl is *stable* because if it is pushed to one side, it will roll back to the center of the bowl again (figure 3.7). A ball on an upside-down bowl is *unstable,* because if it is moved to one side, it will not return but will instead move further away from its original location. A ball on a flat surface, when disturbed, will remain where it is placed, neither returning to its original position nor moving farther away. We say that it is *neutrally stable.* We want the airplane to act like the ball in the bowl and return to normal after being disturbed.

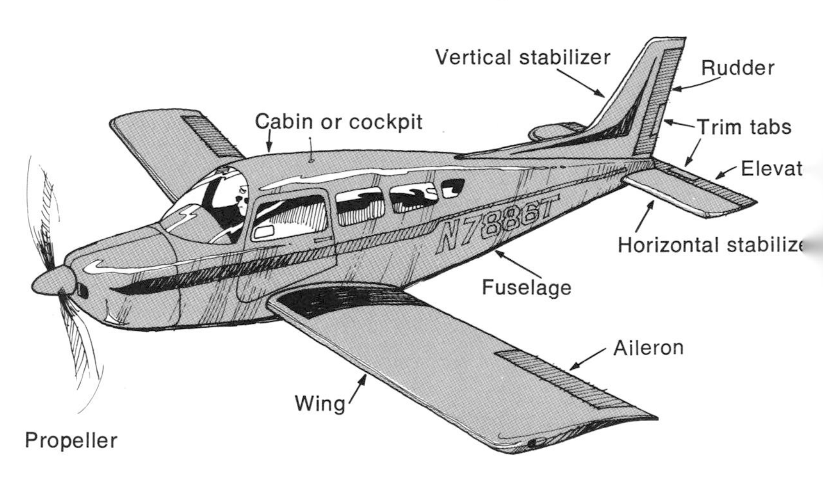

3.6 The basic parts of the airplane

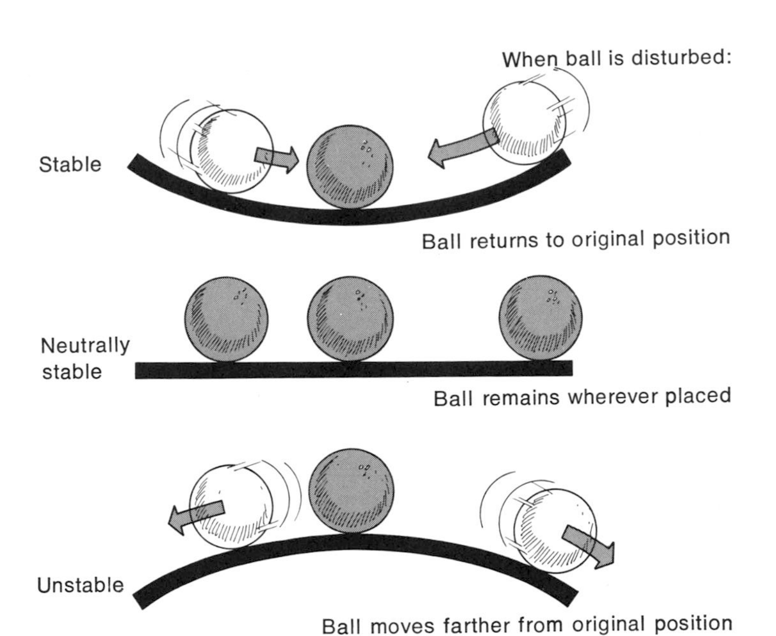

3.7 A stable airplane, like the ball in the top sketch, will return to its original condition after being disturbed.

If you throw a straight stick point first or shoot an arrow that has no feathers, you will find that it will usually tumble or fall end over end as it travels. The stick is probably neutrally stable, that is, if it starts to turn or tumble, there is no force produced to bring it back to traveling point first. A stick can be made into a stable arrow by adding small pieces of feather located along the shaft toward the rear. If an arrow is disturbed in flight and begins to turn, its "tail feathers" acquire an angle of attack and deflect the passing air. The resulting force on the feathers turns the arrow back to a straight path.

An airplane wing, by itself, is unstable. If you try to launch a piece of flat cardboard into a glide, it will not fly smoothly. Most of the time it will flip over and continue to flip end over end as it flutters to the ground. Try to launch just the wing of a model airplane and you will find that the same thing happens. Like the unstable stick, the unstable wing needs some kind of "tail feathers" to balance it and keep it an a straight course.

Most airplanes have their "tail feathers" in the form of a smaller horizontal wing located behind the main wing. Naturally enough, this surface is called the *horizontal stabilizer* (figures 3.6 and 3.8). Properly sized and located, the stabilizer works automatically. When the nose of the airplane moves up, the angle of attack of the horizontal stabilizer also increases, and it pushes air downward to produce lift on this surface. Because it is located a long distance behind the main wing, the increased lift gives it a large "twisting moment" to push the nose down again to level flight. When the airplane is disturbed (by a gust, for example), the stabilizer acts automatically to push the airplane back to its proper attitude.

"But," you might ask, "the horizontal stabilizer on the Wright Brothers' airplane was in *front* of the wing — why?" The answer is that the Wright airplane was not *stable* in pitch but was *controllable* through constant attention by the pilot and use of the movable forward stabilizer. As pointed out earlier, their primary goal was control. They did not make stability a requirement, perhaps not realizing that stability could be obtained at the same time as control. (A little earlier stability was mentioned as a requirement. Although the Wright airplane and others have shown that it is not absolutely essential for flight, it is so highly desirable that we can regard it today as a requirement.)

A few stable airplanes have been built with their horizontal "tail feathers" up front. But it's a bit tricky, and except for some very early airplanes, this arrangement has rarely been used.

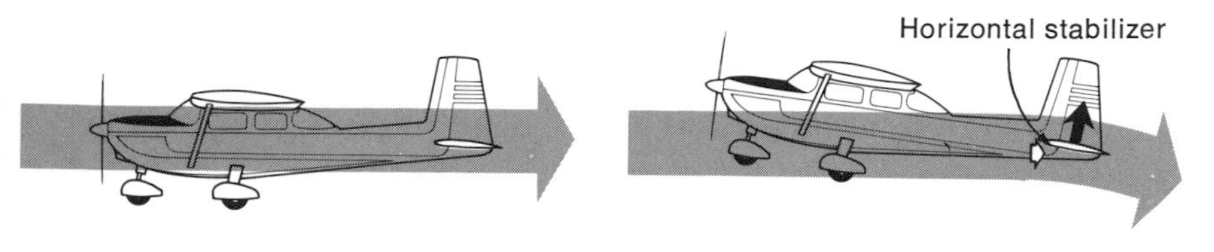

When disturbance changes *pitch* attitude of airplane (nose up or down), force on *horizontal stabilizer* returns airplane to original attitude. (Wing flow omitted for clarity)

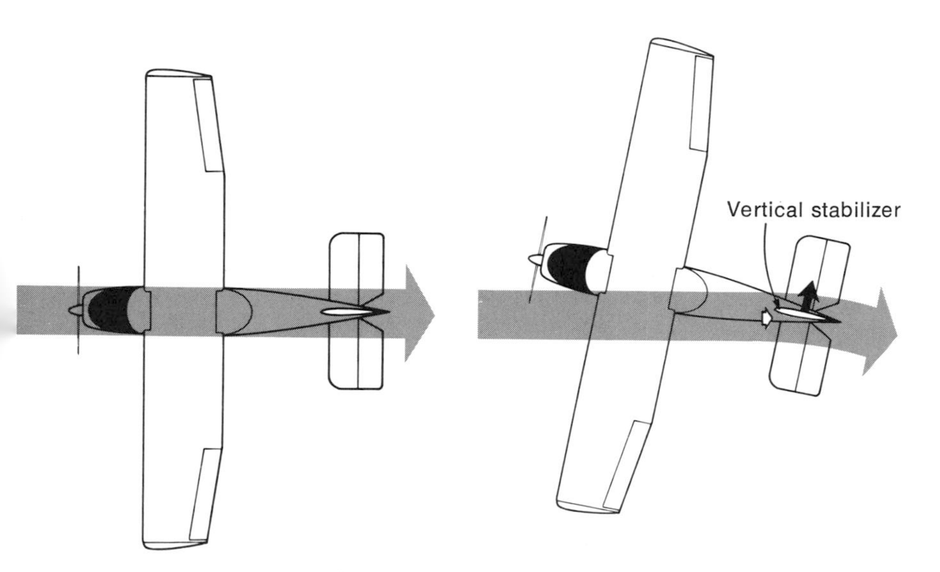

When disturbance changes *yaw* attitude of airplane (nose left or right), force on *vertical stabilizer* returns airplane to original attitude

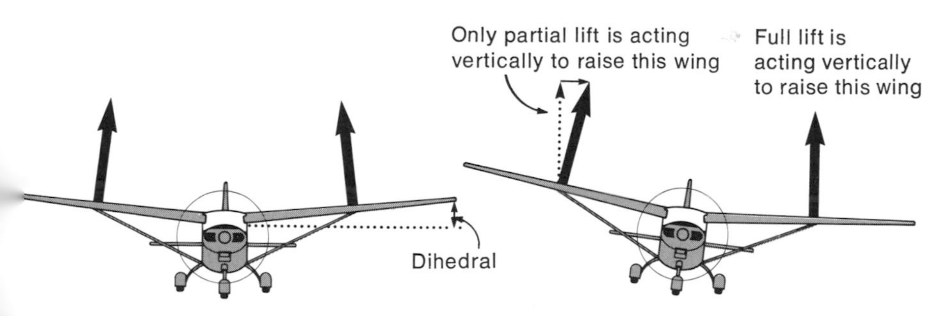

When disturbance changes *lateral* (banked) attitude of airplane, *dihedral* (shown exaggerated) gives lowered wing more lift to return airplane to original attitude

3.8 The airplane's surfaces are designed to provide stability in all directions.

The same gusty air that bumps the airplane nose up or down can bump the airplane into a skid to the right or left. So all airplanes are equipped with some form of *vertical stabilizer,* too. If the airplane's nose swings to the lift, for example, the airstream strikes the right side of the stabilizer and the force developed toward the left twists the airplane back on course (figure 3.8).

The tail surfaces of an airplane thus are not intended to support the airplane in flight, but serve only to balance or stabilize it. We say that the horizontal tail provides *stability in pitch* (nose up and down) and the vertical tail provides *stability in yaw* (nose left and right).

Suppose a gust rolls the airplane by lifting one wing — how can the airplane be designed to return automatically to "wings level" again? To provide *stability in roll,* no extra surfaces are needed, thanks to the discovery of "dihedral" by Sir George Cayley about a hundred years before the first successful airplane. The wings are mounted with a small upward slant, as shown in figure 3.8. In level flight both wings lift equally. But when the airplane is banked, the lowered wing, because it is closer to horizontal, produces more vertical lift than the raised wing. This difference in lift tends to raise the lowered wing again to the level position.

These three kinds of stability help to give the airplane the ability to "fly itself" without constant attention from the pilot.

Close behind the requirement for stability comes the need for *control.* It would do us no good to have an airplane which would only go in the direction in which it was aimed at takeoff — like an arrow — stubbornly resisting our efforts to steer it. We need to be able to make the airplane turn, climb, or glide if it is to take us where we want to go. So in addition to *fixed* tail feathers for stability, the airplane needs some sort of *movable* tail feathers, or control surfaces, which the pilot can use to steer the airplane.

The most important control needed is the *elevator,* which is used to tilt the nose of the airplane up or down, thereby changing the angle of attack of the wing. Elevator control is provided by making the rearward part (or all) of the horizontal stabilizer movable. When the elevator is deflected, it deflects the air passing over it, and a lift force is produced which changes the attitude of the airplane (figure 3.9).

Many people make the mistake of assuming that the elevator is used to make the airplane go up or down. But early in his flight training, every pilot finds that this is simply not true. The elevator control changes the *attitude* of the airplane, but does

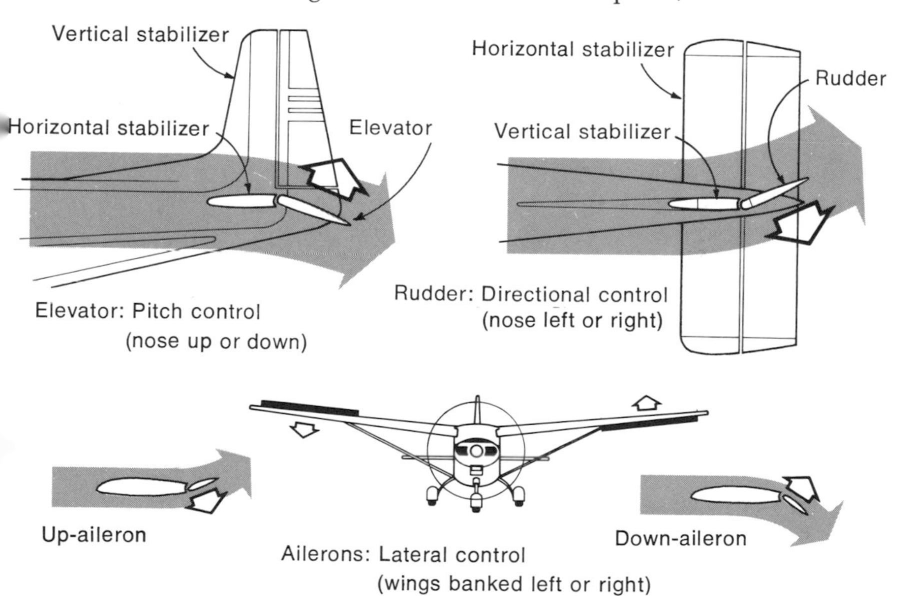

3.9 The airplane's control surfaces, which are hinged portions of the stabilizing or lifting surfaces, deflect air to produce forces in the desired directions.

not necessarily make it climb or glide. Pulling back on the elevator control will increase the angle of attack of the airplane wing (elevator up, nose up, as in the diagram) and make the airplane fly slower; conversely, pushing forward on the control will decrease the angle of attack and will make the airplane fly faster. Whether the airplane will go up, down, or fly level under any condition depends upon how much thrust the engine is producing. It is the engine and propeller that do the work of pulling the airplane up to a higher altitude. So, when the pilot wants to climb, he must first provide enough engine power, and then use the elevator to achieve the climb speed he wants. When he wishes to descend, he must throttle back the engine and, again, set the airplane speed with the elevator.

How does the airplane turn? We have observed that airplanes have rudders, but strangely enough the rudder is *not* used to turn the airplane!

Imagine yourself driving a car across a large ice-covered parking lot. You decide to turn around and go in the opposite direction. If you turn the wheel sharply, the car will not turn, it will only skid sideways. This shows you that a great deal of force is required to turn a heavy car around quickly and head it in the opposite direction. You must make a very gentle turn on ice because the tires of the car will not develop the force needed to let you turn sharply. On a dry parking lot where the tires will grip the pavement, you can turn more sharply without skidding, although the tires may squeal a bit to tell you that they are pushing hard against the pavement to change the car's direction.

Like the automobile, an airplane also needs a large force to change its direction. If only the rudder were used, the airplane would turn slowly, skidding like a car trying to turn on ice. How can an airplane develop a large force with which to change its direction? The wing can produce a tremendous lift force — why not use the wing? That is exactly what is done. The pilot uses the wing for turning by *banking* the plane with his *ailerons*. The ailerons are hinged sections of the wing's trailing edge near the tips that can be moved up or down to decrease or increase the lift of the wing tip (figure 3.9). When the airplane is banked in the direction we wish it to turn, the lift of the wing tilts along with the airplane and pulls it in that direction. The total wing lift can be divided, as shown in figure 3.10, into a vertical component — we might call it useful lift — that supports the airplane and keeps it flying, and a horizontal component that makes the airplane turn. To turn more quickly, the pilot must bank more steeply to make the turning (horizontal) component larger. In order to keep the

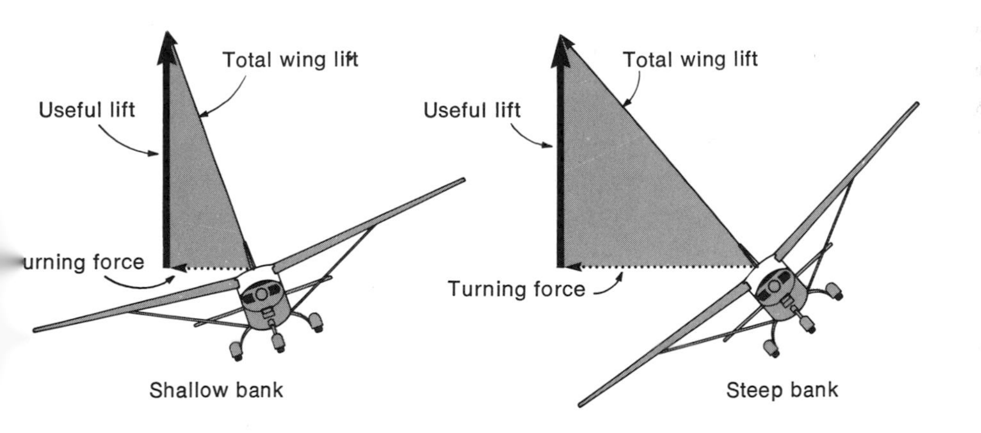

3.10 The pilot can turn more quickly by banking more steeply in order to generate a greater turning force.

vertical part of the lift equal to the weight of the airplane, so that the airplane will not lose altitude, the total lift force of the wing, as the diagram shows, must be larger for the larger angle of bank. This is why pilot and passengers feel squashed down in their seats when the pilot makes a steep turn. The pilot must pull back on the control wheel to put more total lift on the wing while turning steeply.

If it is the wing, not the rudder, that turns an airplane, what is the rudder used for? Not very much, really — in fact some small airplanes have been built with a fixed vertical stabilizer but no rudder at all. The rudder is useful only for making small corrections to hold the airplane on a straight course, for keeping the airplane lined up with the runway during landing and takeoff, and to keep the airplane from skidding while the airplane is being rolled into or out of a banked attitude.

The balance of an airplane is naturally very sensitive to how it is loaded. If an airplane were balanced for full-load conditions, the pilot flying above with no weight in the rear seats or baggage compartment would find his airplane "nose-heavy." As he used fuel from one of his wing tanks, the airplane would tend to lean toward the heavier wing. Because it would be tiresome for the pilot to hold a large control force all during flight to balance his airplane, some form of a "trimming" device is provided. Usually this device consists of another small hinged control surface on each main control surface. The elevator *trim tab,* for example, is mounted at the trailing edge of the elevator. By means of a small wheel or a crank in the cockpit the pilot can change the angle of this tab in either direction. The tab incurs a force from the passing air by deflecting it. This small force, because it has a large "lever arm" at the trailing edge of the elevator, moves the elevator a small amount in the direction necessary to balance the airplane. By adjusting his trim tabs, the pilot can make the airplane fly "hands-off" (no forces needed on the controls) in level flight. He need exert a force on his control only to maneuver from the level flight condition.

Besides the forces that we produce on purpose to lift, stabilize, or turn an airplane, there is one that we would like to avoid producing, but cannot — the force of *drag.* Part of this drag force is *skin friction.* As the airplane moves through the air, the molecules of air rub on its surface and catch on all the rough edges and protuberances, exerting a drag force that tends to hold the airplane back. This drag is inescapable because friction occurs whenever two substances (in this case air and the airplane) rub together. The designer tries to reduce this drag to a minimum by making all surfaces smooth and well streamlined.

The other part of the drag force comes from wing lift. As the wing deflects air downward to produce lift, the total reaction lift force (figure 3.11, top) is not exactly vertical, but is tilted slightly rearward. This means that it contains some rearward, or drag, force. We can see this force by breaking down the reaction force into a vertical force, which is useful lift, and a horizontal force, which is drag. This drag, called *drag due to lift* or *induced drag,* is, you might say, the price we pay to produce lift. As we might guess from the top sketch of figure 3.11, the larger the angle of attack, the more the reaction-force on the wing tilts to the rear, and the larger the drag due to lift becomes. Good design can reduce this drag, but not eliminate it. We might guess, again, that efficient wings that operate at low angles of attack will have less drag due to lift. Long, tapered wings are more efficient than short, stubby ones, for example, which is why high-performance sailplanes have extremely large wingspans.

We have seen that the airplane's motion — the flow of air past its surfaces — makes it possible for the airplane to generate the needed lift and control forces. We have also seen that this motion is opposed by drag forces. We must therefore provide a forward force — a propulsive thrust — to overcome this drag and keep the airplane in motion.

An airplane cannot produce its propulsive force by pushing against something solid, as an automobile can against the ground. The airplane has only air to push against, and as we know, air will not stand still. The propeller makes it possible for the airplane to move itself through the air. The propeller is really a lifting surface, like a wing, traveling in a circle. It is

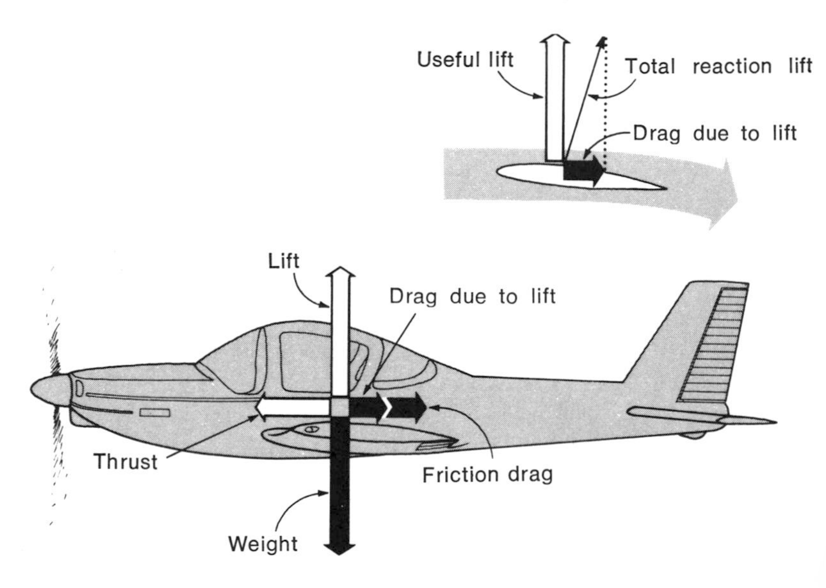

3.11 The forces on an airplane must be in equilbrium for level flight: lift = weight, thrust = drag.

twisted so that all parts meet the air at a similar angle of attack, even though these parts are all traveling different "corkscrew" paths at different speeds. The propeller slices into the air and accelerates air backwards toward the rear of the airplane. Here we meet again Newton's third law of motion, which says that a backward acceleration of the air (the action) will be matched by a forward push on the propeller (the reaction). This reaction is the thrust we want.

The forces on all parts of the airplane are too complex if we try to look at all of them, but we can combine them into four main forces: thrust, lift, drag, and weight (figure 3.11, bottom). In steady flight these forces must cancel each other, or add up to zero, as we say. The lift must equal the weight, while the total drag must be overcome by a propulsive thrust. When the forces are thus in equilibrium, there will be no force changing the airplane's speed or flight path.

Each part of an airplane, fixed or movable, must be carefully designed to push air in just the right ways to produce the forces needed for flight. We can think of every airplane, from the wood-and-fabric model of fifty years ago to the supersonic jet of today, regardless of its shape, size, or purpose, as being just a bundle of air deflectors, nothing more.

4

Engines, Propellers, and Jets

MAN'S AMBITION TO FLY by his own muscle power is not quite dead. Anyone who thinks that he can do it can try for a prize of $28,000 and whatever fame would come along with it. All he has to do is to build a man-powered airplane which can take off, fly at an altitude of at least ten feet on a figure-eight course around two pylons one-half mile apart, and return to the starting point. His crew can consist of any number of people, and all may contribute their muscle power, but no hidden engines or other monkey business will be permitted.

The prize is offered by an English industrialist, Mr. Henry Kremer. A number of very clever machines have been built for this contest in the past ten years, most of them in England. But no one has yet won the prize. Most of the entries were very efficient, extremely lightweight machines, built of such materials as spruce, balsa wood, and thin plastic sheeting and driven by pedals and propeller. Ornithopters seem to have been abandoned. Several craft have succeeded in getting off the ground for short flights, but one pilot who pedaled a more or less straight half-mile test flight freely admitted that the half mile was his absolute limit.

All of the contestants know what a difficult job they have tackled. They look upon the contest as an interesting engineering challenge, not as a goal having practical value. In some designs the contestants attempted to multiply their muscle power with gearing. They were doomed to disappointment, of course. Either speed or force can be increased by gearing, but the laws of nature make it impossible for us to increase power. If it were possible to increase a man's power with gears, it would also be possible to gear up a lawn-mower engine to drive a locomotive.

Though someone may someday claim the prize, the Kremer competition should provide final proof, if such is needed, that man's muscle power, compared to his weight, is simply not enough for practical flight. From actual measurements we know that a man can develop about one horsepower for a very short time. Working steadily, he can produce only about 1/8 horsepower — about as much power as it takes to light a 100-watt reading lamp. Even if we use the best aeronautical skills and the best in lightweight materials and structures, this much horsepower is not enough. The inescapable forces of gravity and friction will require man to use a mechanical power plant for practical flight.

The Wright Brothers calculated that they needed about eight horsepower to lift their powered glider into the air. They wasted no time thinking about muscle power, but planned instead to use a gasoline engine. The gasoline engine was then only in its infancy. Only small motors were being built, mostly for automobiles. No one had thought very much about motors for flight, and the Wrights had to build their own, as we saw in an earlier chapter. The problem that they faced in the design of their engine was the same problem that airplane-engine designers have struggled with ever since — how to build the lightest, most reliable engine for the required horsepower. The Wrights were the first to prove that a gasoline engine light enough to drive a man-carrying airplane could be built. Their choice of a *four-stroke-cycle* engine was a good one. This kind of engine powered nearly all aircraft for forty years after its development, and is still used in most small airplanes. It is also the kind of engine most used in automobiles.

In the four-stroke cycle there are four separate operations within the engine's cylinders, as shown in figure 4.1. In the intake stroke, the piston moves downward and draws in air which has been mixed with fuel vapor at the carburetor. In the compression stroke, the piston rams the fuel-air mixture into a smaller space to get it ready for burning. A spark from the spark plug ignites the mixture near the beginning of the power stroke, and the pressure of the hot burning gases pushes the piston downward to deliver power to the engine. On its return, the piston pushes the spent gases out of the cylinder into the atmosphere. The piston then moves down again to draw in another fresh charge of air and fuel vapor for the next cycle.

The amount of power that an engine can produce depends upon how much air and fuel it can burn, which depends, in turn, upon the size of its cylinders and how rapidly it fills and empties those cylinders. A model airplane with a single cylinder as big as your thumb may put out only a fraction of a horsepower, while a multicylinder airplane engine with cylinders the size of wastebaskets may develop several thousand horsepower.

As airplane designers worked to build airplanes with more speed and more lifting power, engine designers worked to provide them with larger, more powerful engines. Many of the early engines were water-cooled. Like the automobile engines of today, they were built with passages around the cylinders through which water could be pumped to carry off engine heat. A radiator was needed to convey the heat from the hot water into the surrounding air. The engine with its radiator and plumbing was very heavy, and the large radiator mounted in the airstream on the fuselage or between the wings added a great deal of drag. Sometimes a designer placed a larger engine in his airplane only to find that most of the increased power was used up in simply pulling the engine and its larger radiator through the air!

The air-cooled airplane engine eliminated the radiator and

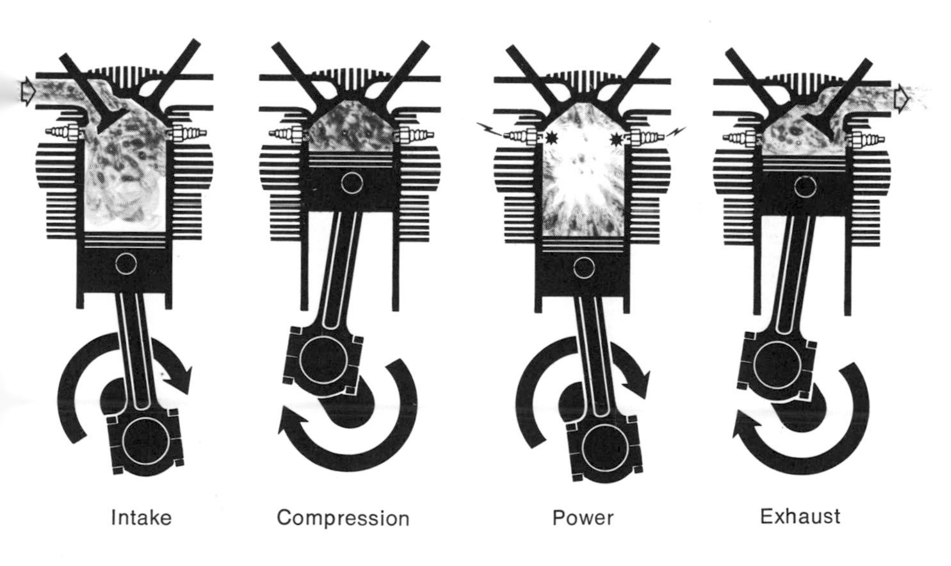

4.1 Strokes of the four-stroke-cycle engine

plumbing of the water-cooled engine. Instead of a heavy liquid cooling system, this engine had thin fins of metal on its cylinders and other parts to conduct heat directly into the air that passed over the cylinders. The air-cooled engine quickly became popular, and has been more widely used than any other piston engine.

Most of the larger air-cooled engines are the *radial* type, that is, with cylinders mounted around the crankcase like the spokes of a wheel (figure 4.2). The early air-cooled engines still had a great deal of drag if the airstream was allowed to flow over them directly, so engines were built into tight-fitting, streamlined "cowlings" as airplanes became faster and more streamlined.

As the need for more engine power continued, larger radial engines were designed with a double row of cylinders. Engines

4.2 The radial engine

COURTESY OF PRATT AND WHITNEY AIRCRAFT

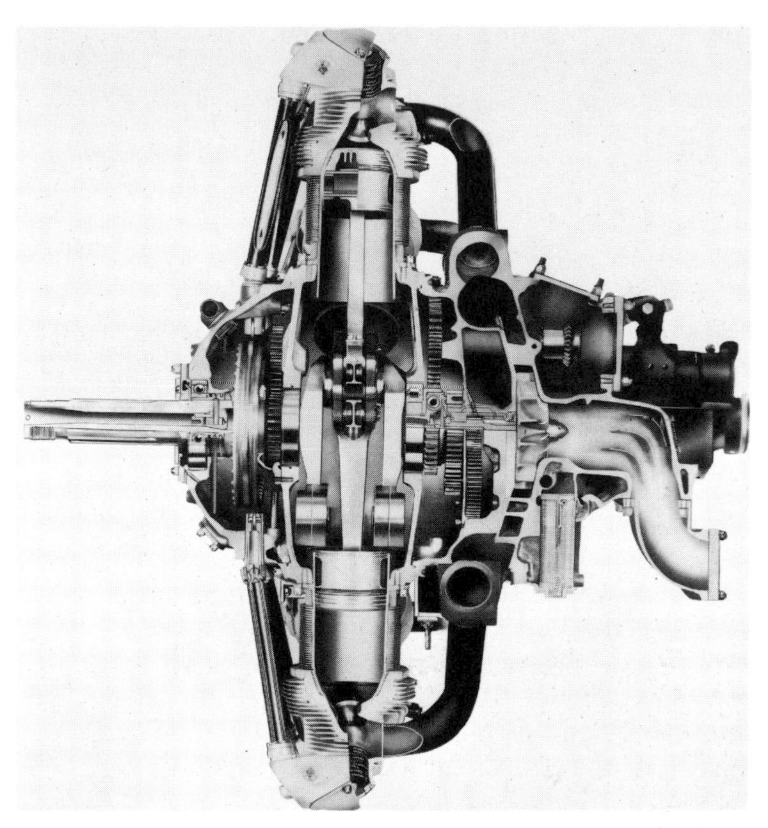

The radial engine

of this type were used on American World War II bombers such as the B-17, B-24, and B-29. Large commercial transports powered by these engines carried airline passengers all over the world, before being replaced by jet-powered airliners.

The largest piston engine ever built in America was a radial air-cooled engine (figure 4.3). Dubbed the "corncob" for its thirty-six cylinders mounted in four rows, it could gulp a roomful of air in fifteen or twenty seconds and produce 3,500 horsepower. Although the need existed for still more powerful engines, the piston engine had about reached its maximum practical size in the "corncob."

As airplane speeds increased, engineers began to see trouble ahead. They knew that the engine-propeller unit can put out a constant amount of horsepower at all speeds. *Power,* which is the rate at which the engine can do *work,* is measured by multiplying thrust force by speed. With its constant horsepower, therefore, the engine-propeller unit can produce a large thrust force at a small speed or a small thrust force at a high speed. And so at the higher speeds where *more* thrust was needed, the engine-propeller was giving *less!* Adding more engines would help, but four engines seemed to be a practical limit even for very large airplanes. The end of the road was approaching. Four hundred and fifty miles per hour seemed to be the highest practical speed that could be reached by airplanes powered by piston engines and propellers.

The propeller itself was beginning to give trouble, too, but for a different reason. It had about reached its limit of size and speed because of the problem of *tip speed.* The blades of a propeller always travel faster than the airplane itself because they have two simultaneous motions: they travel forward with the airplane, and travel in a circle as they rotate. Figure 4.4 shows how these speeds add up and why the propeller has its characteristic twisted shape.

The parts of the propeller blade near the hub travel in a small circle while moving forward with the airplane, and their total speed is only a little more than airplane speed. But the tip of the propeller travels in a huge circle as it moves forward and its total speed can be very high. At an airplane speed of only 350 miles per hour, the tips of the propeller may approach the speed of sound, which is about 760 miles per hour at sea level.

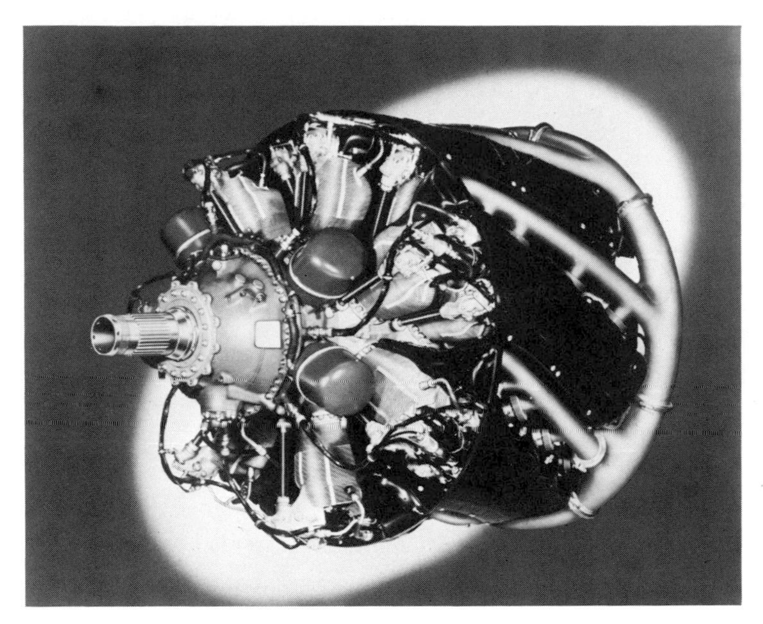

4.3 A four-row radial engine
COURTESY OF PRATT AND WHITNEY AIRCRAFT

For reasons which will be discussed in detail in Chapter 13, the shock waves that occur near sonic speed cause vibration, loss of thrust, and poor propeller performance.

Both the piston engine and propeller thus were in trouble at high speeds and engineers thought for a time that further increases in airplane speeds would be impossible to attain. Unless, of course, a new kind of propulsion could be developed. Back in 1922 a new idea called *jet propulsion* had appeared in a report published by the United States Bureau of Standards. Because it was predicted that this engine would use *four times* as much fuel as a good engine-propeller system at 250 miles per hour, no one was very much interested in jet propulsion at that time.

The report predicted, however, that efficiency would improve

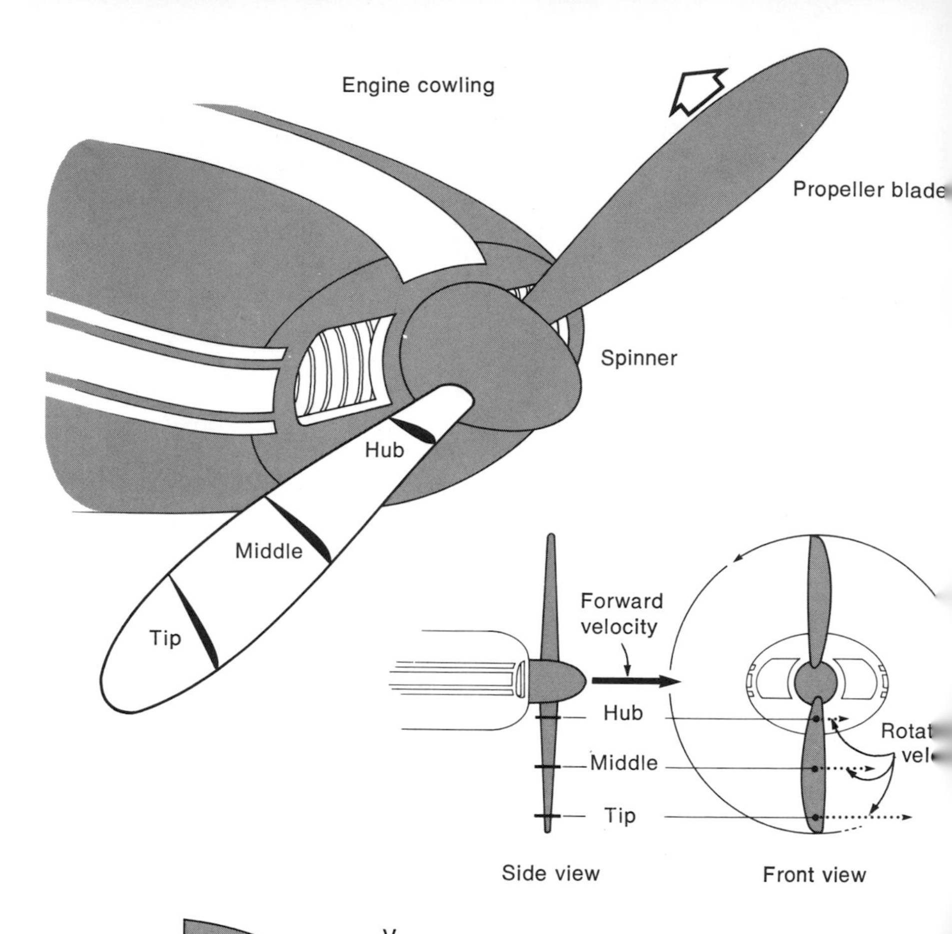

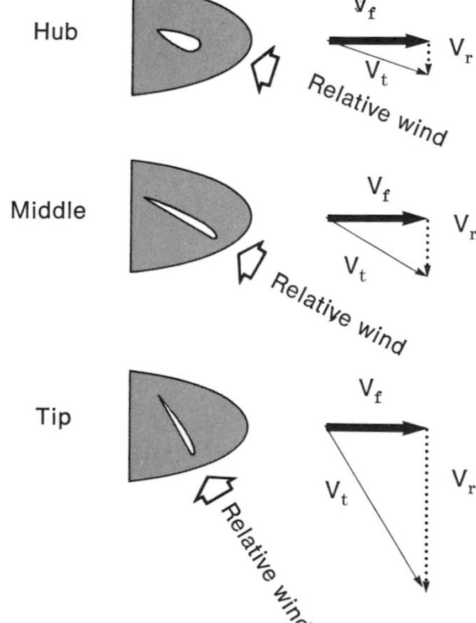

1) Forward velocity, V_f, is same for
   parts of the propeller
2) Rotational velocity, V_r, is differ
   for each part, larger toward th
   because it whirls in a larger circ
3) Resultant or total velocity, V_t, is
   sum of the two velocities for ea
   part, and has the direction show
4) The relative wind strikes the prop
   in exactly the opposite direction
5) The propeller blade at each po
   is aligned to the relative wind
   the proper angle of attack, thu
   giving twist to the propeller as s

4.4 The propeller is designed
a "twist" because each. pa
travels a different path thro
the air.

at higher speeds. Now that higher speeds were in sight, engineers began to look again at this new kind of propulsion. A British engineer, Colonel Frank Whittle, was the first to do serious work on the new engine. He developed the first aircraft *turbojet engine* in England in the late 1930's. The United States quickly became interested, and the first American jet-propelled airplane, the Bell Airacomet, powered with American-built Whittle engines, took to the air in 1942.

The turbojet engine (figure 4.5) is based upon the same cycle and the same principles as the piston engine, yet it does its job in a different way. Figure 4.6 shows how the same four

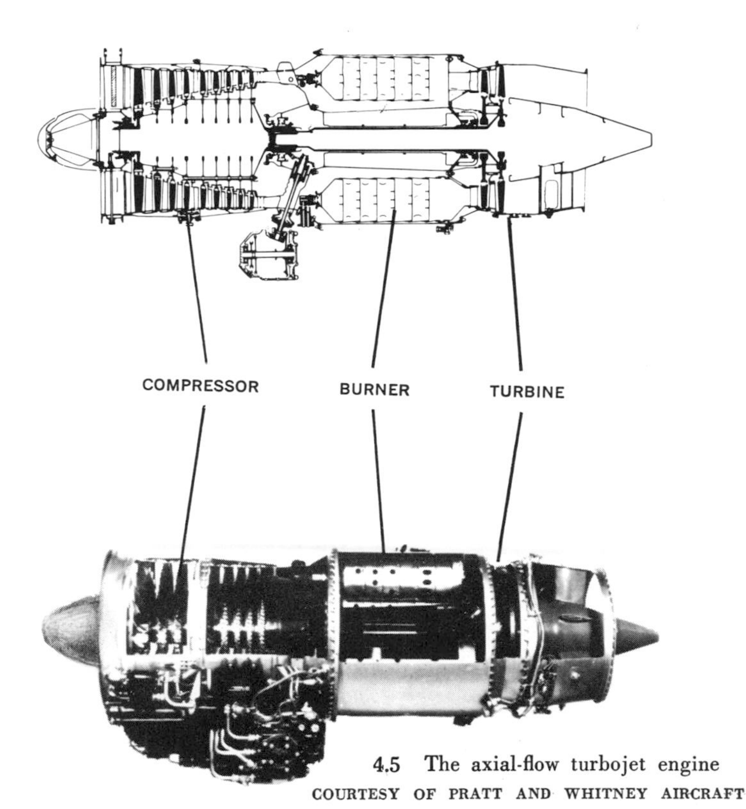

4.5 The axial-flow turbojet engine
COURTESY OF PRATT AND WHITNEY AIRCRAFT

"strokes" of the piston engine cycle are used in the jet-engine cycle. For the intake stroke, the air flows into the front part of the engine. In the compression stroke, a series of whirling blades jams the air into a smaller space. Next, fuel is sprayed into the compressed air and ignited at the beginning of the power stroke. The hot high-pressure gases roar toward the rear, twisting a turbine wheel as they rush past it. The turbine takes out only part of the "push" of the gases, using this power to turn the compressor blades up front. The gases continue their rush out through the tail pipe to exhaust into the atmosphere.

It is easy to see, in the case of the piston engine, that the hot gases push on the *piston* to produce power. But what do the gases in the jet engine push against? The answer is that the gases push on the *whole engine* — just as though the engine

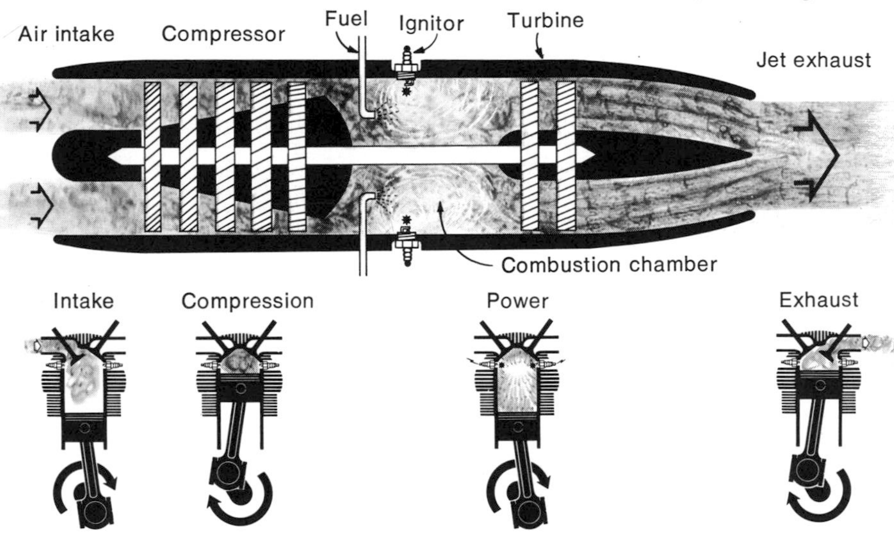

4.6 The turbojet-engine cycle has the same elements as the piston-engine cycle.

were a giant piston. And instead of pushing on a piston for only part of the cycle, the continuous flow of gases gives the jet engine — and the airplane — a steady push forward.

We can look at both the jet engine and the propeller as examples of Newton's third law of motion: "For every action there is an equal and opposite reaction." The engine "acts" upon the air by compressing it, heating it with burning fuel, and blasting it rearward out of the exhaust. This action produces a "reaction," according to Newton's law, which is a forward push, or thrust, on the engine.

"Where is the propeller?" someone was always asking during the early years of the jet engine. While it might be correct to say that there *isn't* any propeller, it's a little more accurate to say that it's inside. The jet engine is both engine and propeller, all in one. It uses the same air for both burning and propulsion. The engine-propeller combination, on the other hand, uses air inside the engine for burning and air outside for propulsion.

The jet engine solved two problems that had been plaguing airplane designers: it got rid of the propeller with its sonic troubles, and it got rid of the clusmy piston-and-cylinder arrangement that made piston engines big and heavy and full of vibrations. The jet engine doesn't stop to compress and burn a wastebasketful of fuel-air mixture at a time in each cylinder; instead it takes in a great torrent of air, compresses it, mixes it with fuel, and burns it as it roars through the engine, then flings it rearward without stopping it at all.

The jet engine is light in weight and can gulp many times as much air as a piston engine of the same size. Because of its great power, the jet engine can be mistakenly thought to operate on a different basic principle, or to be somehow more efficient than the piston engine. The thing to remember is that the jet engine produces greater thrust because it can handle more air and therefore burn more fuel. Because it burns fuel at such a rapid rate, the jet-powered airplane must fly high, where there is less air resistance, and it must fly fast because it cannot fly for a long time. The turbojet engine therefore is not a practical engine for a small, low-speed, low-altitude airplane, which is why no such airplane has ever been built with turbojet engines. We can see that turbojet engines* would be even less suitable as power plants for trains or automobiles.

The turbojet engine had another very pleasant surprise for the airplane designer: it gave him the thrust he needed to fly at very high speeds. As mentioned earlier, the piston engine–propeller combination is a constant-power machine whose thrust becomes smaller at high speeds just when it is needed the most. But the jet engine is a *constant-thrust* machine. Its thrust can stay nearly constant up to flight speeds near the speed of sound. At still higher speeds the compression of the air entering the engine helps it to provide an even greater thrust. Here, as you will quickly recognize, was the engine that might make supersonic flight possible!

It wasn't long before engineers discovered how to get even *more* power from the turbojet. The engine normally burns only enough fuel to consume one-third to one-quarter of the oxygen in the air it takes in. If it burned more than this, gas temperatures inside the engine would become too high for even the special high-temperature metals from which the engine is built. With an *afterburner* added to the engine, military airplanes could use a short burst of extra power for takeoff, climb,

* *Not to be confused with* gas-turbine engines *which drive the vehicle through its wheels and are quite suitable for this use.*

or a supersonic dash. This special device is a second combustion chamber, located between the engine and the jet tail pipe. Fuel sprayed into the jet of hot gases at this point mixes with the remaining oxygen and burns to produce still more thrust. The afterburner is not as efficient as the engine itself; consequently, the increased thrust is very costly in fuel. But for special purposes, the afterburner is often worthwhile.

Although the turbojet engine solved some important problems, it also created a few new ones. Because the jet engine produces its thrust by giving a relatively small-diameter stream of air a tremendous rearward acceleration, the searing exhaust that roars from the tail pipe contains an enormous amount of energy. You can hear this energy — and even feel it — as noise. Communities located near airports have become more and more concerned as more and more powerful jet engines have increased the noise of departing jet traffic to earsplitting levels.

The energy in the jet also represents wasted energy. If the jet engine could handle a larger amount of air — as a large-diameter propeller might, for example — it could produce its thrust by giving this larger amount of air a more gentle push backwards. The smaller amount of energy in the jet exhaust would mean less noise, less wasted energy, and greater propulsive efficiency.

The *turbofan engine* is a relatively new kind of jet engine that helps to solve both of these problems, and a few more besides. The turbofan engine is like a turbojet engine with a small propeller added (figure 4.7). The first row (or rows) of blades — called the fan — has a larger diameter than the turbojet part of the engine, and handles an extra volume of air. This extra air passes around the rest of the engine through special fan

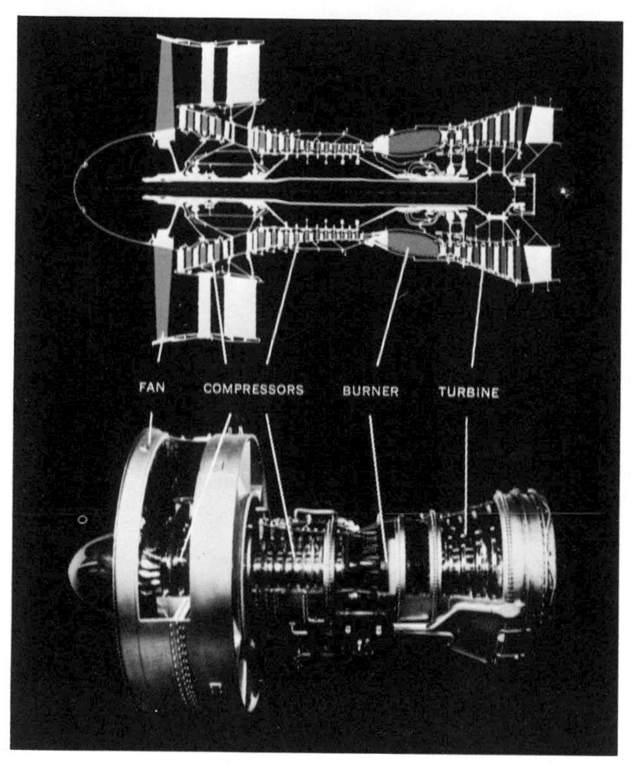

4.7 The turbofan engine

COURTESY OF PRATT AND WHITNEY AIRCRAFT

ducts. The air passing through the center of the fan continues through the rest of the compressor stages, through the burners and turbine, to become the hot jet exhaust.

Because this engine handles a great deal more air than the conventional turbojet, it can give this air a smaller acceleration, and less energy. With less energy in its exhaust jet, the turbofan engine can be both quieter and more efficient than a simple turbojet engine of the same power. As an extra bonus, the fan improves engine operation by producing more thrust at takeoff and climb speeds, and by allowing cool fan air to flow over the hot parts of the engine.

The *turboprop engine* (figure 4.8) is much like the turbojet engine, and perhaps even more like a turbofan engine. But it is different from both in that a large portion of the power of the engine gases is taken out by the turbine and used to drive an external propeller. Gearing makes it possible for the propeller to turn at a slow speed while the compressor and turbine, like those of the turbojet, rotate at extremely high speed. After the exhaust gases go through the turbine, they are exhausted rearward to provide jet thrust that adds to the thrust of the propeller.

The turboprop engine has less weight and fewer vibrations than the piston engine, and has almost entirely replaced the piston engine on large airplanes designed for medium altitudes, short flights, and speeds up to about 400 miles per hour, where an external propeller is an advantage.

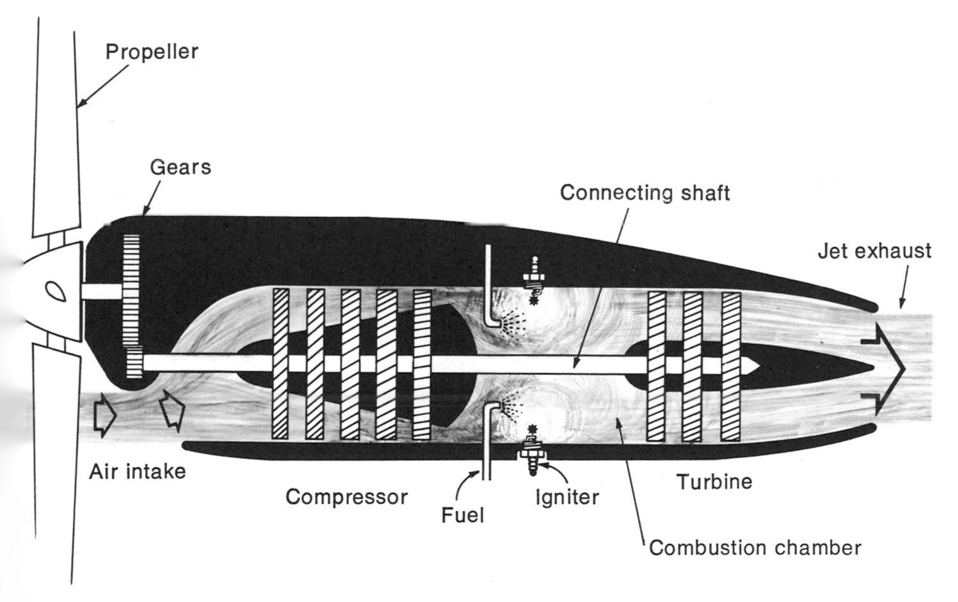

4.8 The turboprop engine

The *ramjet engine* and the *rocket* are not ordinarily used as aircraft engines, but we might look at them briefly because they do have special uses. The ramjet becomes interesting at very high speeds (three times the speed of sound or more). At these speeds the forward motion of the aircraft (or missile) will compress the air without the need for whirling blades. The ramjet engine looks more like a piece of stovepipe than an engine. As the air rams its way into the front end, fuel is burned in the compressed air, which then expands and roars out through the other end to produce thrust. Although ramjets are basically simple and light in weight, they have a number of problems. They must be accelerated to high supersonic speed by another means — a turbojet engine or a rocket, for example — before they can be started. Their fuel consumption is high, and they must be operated at extremely high temperatures in order to be at all practical. Flown only in a few missiles, the ramjet has not proved to be widely useful. But for flight at hypersonic speeds, five times the speed of sound and higher, the ramjet might be the engine to use.

The rocket engine is useful in aircraft only to provide great thrust for a very short time, as in research airplanes. The first airplane to exceed the speed of sound, the X-1, was rocket-powered because it was built before powerful jet engines were available.

The X-15 was designed to probe speed ranges up to five times the speed of sound and altitudes up to the very edge of space; consequently, the rocket engine was the only propulsion that could be used. Such airplanes have very short operating periods because of enormous fuel consumption. The X-15 engine can consume nearly ten tons of propellant in less than two minutes. The rocket carries its own oxygen (or oxidizer) — a requirement in space but a disadvantage for flight in the atmosphere where oxygen need not be carried on board but can be picked up as needed.

Power has been the key item in aviation progress since the very beginning. Twelve horsepower lifted the first airplane and its pilot into the air. A light airplane today may use from 100 to 300 horsepower. A military fighter airplane may need 20,000 to 40,000 horsepower to blast it through the air at supersonic speeds. A jumbo jet may use 65,000 horsepower to cruise at high subsonic speeds, while a large supersonic transport would need over half a million horsepower to cruise at three times the speed of sound.

Powerful engines alone would be useless to us if there were no suitable airplanes for them to propel. Swift progress in aerodynamics, materials, and structures has kept airplane development abreast of engine development, and has given us airplanes today that are very different from their early ancestors.

5

From Ancestors Made of Rags and Sticks

THE FIRST AIRPLANES were built in the days of the horse and buggy, and they looked it. They were made of horse-and-buggy materials — wood, cloth, and bits of metal — the lightest materials of that day. Lightweight metals like aluminum and magnesium were not yet available, and plastics and high-strength steels had not yet been invented. No one knew quite how to design lightweight aircraft structures, either, and some early airplanes were designed with structures copied from bridges.

The first airplanes were as unstreamlined as a buggy, too. The pilot lay or sat in the open, surrounded by a maze of struts and wires. The engine and its radiator also sat boldly in the open airstream. The early designers probably guessed that their crude arrangements were good enough. At the speeds they were hoping to reach — 40 to 60 miles per hour — streamlining didn't matter very much. Their main problem was to design a machine that would get off the ground and fly safely.

But all airplanes builders were soon caught up in the race to build the airplane that could travel fastest, highest, or farthest, or could carry the largest load — a race that still goes on today. As more powerful engines made more speed available, designers began to notice that a great deal of power was being wasted in pulling unstreamlined shapes through the air. They began to design airplanes with a hollow body, called a *fuselage,* from a French word meaning "spindle-shaped." On this fuselage they mounted the wings, the tail surfaces, and the engine. The place where the pilot sat was called the cockpit. Even with a windshield mounted ahead of it, the open cockpit was a drafty place, and could get very cold in winter weather. The development of the cabin airplane was a great improvement, giving the pilot and passengers a sheltered place to sit where they might even have a heater to take the chill off. Today the only airplanes built with open cockpits are for sport purposes, and for crop dusting and spraying, where the pilot needs to be able to see all around him.

The nose of the fuselage was soon found to be a logical place for the engine and propeller. The air could flow freely over the engine there to keep it cool and the propeller could whirl in undisturbed air. The "tractor" airplane became the most common arrangement: engine and propeller up front, one or two (or even three!) wings attached to the fuselage, and tail surfaces at the rear.

Airplanes were still fairly flimsy, primitive things at the beginning of World War I, but they proved so useful that all countries worked hard to improve their warplanes. Although the airplane was an American invention, European warplanes were so far ahead of American machines that nearly all combat flying during World War I was done with airplanes made in Europe.

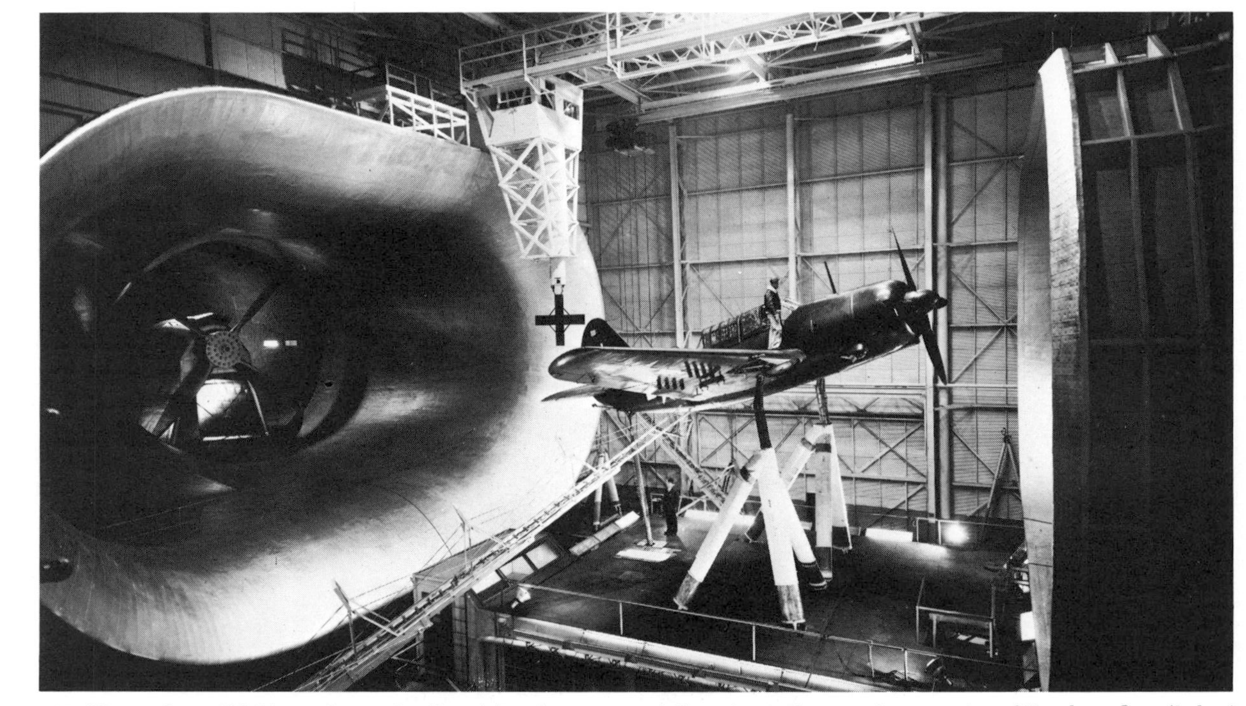

5.1 Views of two NASA wind tunnels. One (above) can test a full-scale airplane at low speeds, while the other (below) is designed to test a two-foot-span model in a wind stream traveling at 2½ times the speed of sound.

COURTESY OF NASA

To prevent American aviation from continuing to lag behind the rest of the world, Congress in 1915 created the National Advisory Committee for Aeronautics (NACA) "to supervise and direct the scientific study of the problems of flight, with a view to their practical solution." After the war, both industry and government began to devote more and more effort to research and development in aeronautics.

Strong new alloys of lightweight metals such as aluminum and magnesium were developed. Every pound of weight that could be saved meant an extra pound of payload or fuel that could be carried. Structural engineers struggled with new ways of designing the airplane's wings, fuselage, and control surfaces to make them as light in weight as possible, yet strong enough to do the job. To check their new ideas, they built sample wings and other structures and tested them in the laboratory — loading, twisting, and vibrating them until they ripped apart.

Aerodynamics engineers needed a way of testing new shapes for wings, new ideas for controls, and new airplane designs. The crude low-speed wind tunnel of the Wright Brothers had given useful answers, but the aviation world now needed more measurements, better accuracy, more speed. Wind tunnels of many sizes and types were built for testing and research. A few were built large enough to test a full-sized airplane (figure 5.1), but most were designed for testing small models of airplanes or airplane parts.

Propulsion engineers worked for better fuels and lubricants, lightweight high-strength metals and metals to withstand the high temperatures inside the aircraft engine. They studied the processes of combustion and cooling in order to better understand what went on inside their engines. Test engines howled night and day for weeks on test stands to prove their reliability.

Engine parts that failed or wore out were improved and retested. Always the researchers were seeking power, efficiency, reliability, and light weight for their engines.

As engines became larger and speeds higher, designers found that the engine added a great deal of drag. Rushing past the maze of cylinders, fins, rods, wires, and pipes that make up the engine, the air pulls and tugs at each one, and greatly slows airplane speed. In 1928 NACA made one of its most famous early discoveries in the aeronautical field. Research engineers placed a full-sized airplane in a giant NACA wind tunnel and measured its drag. Then they covered the radial engine with a streamlined metal shroud they called a "cowling" and again measured the airplane's drag. To everyone's astonishment, they found that the cowling decreased the drag sufficiently to increase the airplane's speed from 120 miles per hour to about 140 miles per hour. The engine ran cooler, too, because the air entered the cowling slowly and flowed smoothly over the engine inside. Designers quickly took advantage of this discovery and began to mount engines out of the wind stream in streamlined cowlings.

It was soon recognized that the maze of struts and wires that held most early airplanes together would make high speeds impossible no matter how much power was used (figure 5.2). Using fewer struts and wires and making them streamlined helped to reduce the drag, but designers knew that eventually all external bracing must be eliminated. New lightweight alloys of aluminum and new ideas on wing design came to the rescue. All-metal wings were designed that had strong beams inside and a thin metal "skin" that added to the strength of the whole wing. These wings needed no struts and wires in the airstream at all. We can see from this example how engineers in the fields

5.2 The Curtiss NC-4, first airplane to fly across the Atlantic Ocean, May

COURTESY OF NATIONAL AIR AND SPACE MUSEUM, SMITHSONIAN INSTITUTION

of materials, structures, and aerodynamics all worked together to "clean up" and streamline the airplane for higher and higher performance.

The landing gear was another "drag-catcher." In order to be able to take off, land and taxi on the ground, an airplane had to pull the wheels and their supports through the air during the entire flight. The solution to this problem was found only fifteen years after the birth of the airplane: design the landing gear so that it could be pulled up inside the airplane where it would have *no* drag. The mechanism to do this added more weight, but the increase in airplane speed saved enough fuel to make the retractable landing gear worthwhile. Most airplanes today that fly over 150 miles per hour are built with retractable landing gears.

As airplane speeds increased, the propeller began to give trouble. The twist that a propeller needs depends upon both the propeller speed and forward speed of the airplane, as we saw in figure 4.4. If the propeller was designed for the slow speeds of takeoff and climb, its twist was incorrect for cruising speed. As a result, engine power was wasted and the airplane did not reach as high a speed as it should. On the other hand, if the propeller was designed for the higher cruising speeds, its takeoff and climb performance was poor — perhaps dangerously so. Propellers consequently were designed with a twist that was a compromise between takeoff and cruise conditions. Such a propeller worked fairly well for both conditions but was not the best for either. As cruising speed was pushed farther from takeoff speed, the loss in propeller performance became very serious.

The *variable-pitch propeller* was invented in 1932, and was an immediate success. Instead of a clumsy fixed blade carved from wood, the variable pitch propeller had metal blades mounted in a hub so that they could be twisted by a control in the cockpit (figure 5.3). The blades could be set at one pitch for takeoff, then twisted to a new setting for cruise. The improvement in airplane performance was so great that variable-pitch propellers have been used ever since for nearly all aircraft designed for a speed of more than about 150 miles per hour.

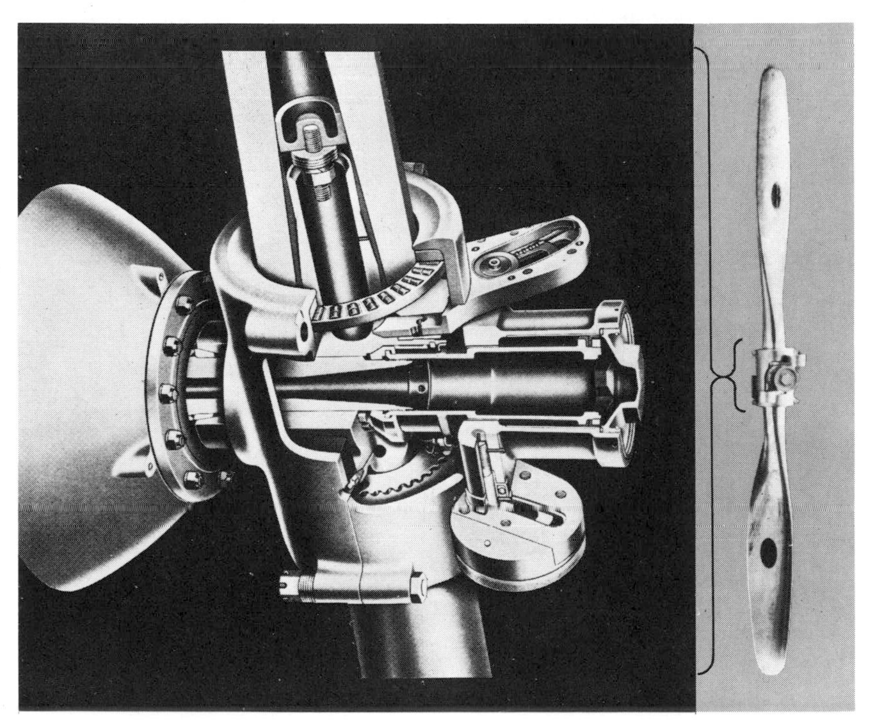

5.3 The blades of a controllable-pitch propeller can be twisted in the hub in flight in order to achieve the best pitch setting for every flight speed.

COURTESY OF HAMILTON STANDARD DIVISION, UNITED AIRCRAFT CORPORATION

As the big things — the engine, wires, struts, landing gear — were moved out of the airstream, the *little* things that can cause drag came under scrutiny. Rivets and rough surfaces, metal edges that stuck up into the airstream, leaks in the surface where air could squirt in or out, all proved to be important, and airplane builders strove to make airplanes more smooth and streamlined.

Research engineers began to look closely at the "boundary layer" — that layer of air a fraction of an inch deep that rubs on the airplane's surface — and to ponder how they might keep the boundary layer from causing trouble. As air flows over a surface, the particles closest to the surface rub on it and are slowed down. Particles a little farther from the surface are slowed down much less, and continue to move past the others. If the surface is smooth and nothing disturbs the flow, these particles, or layers, of air near the surface "slip" with respect to each other but do not mix. This is called *laminar* flow, which means "arranged in thin layers." This kind of flow, with its thin layers of air slipping smoothly over each other, in effect "protects" the surface from excessive friction, and causes the least amount of drag. But if the air flows along a surface for a long distance, or if the surface is rough, the air closest to the surface slows so much that it may "trip up" the other outer layers and begin to mix with them. As little whirls and eddies form and spread outward, the boundary layer becomes *turbulent* and grows much deeper (figure 5.4). More air is scrubbed against the surface of the airplane because of the tiny eddies in this turbulent flow, and more drag results.

Turbulent flow with its tiny eddies should not be confused with separated flow, in which the air no longer follows the surface but tears away to form large swirls and regions of "dead air." Separated or stalled flow on a wing, for example, is a large-sized faulty flow that causes loss of lift and a large increase in drag. Turbulent flow is merely a thicker layer of air that is still reasonably well-behaved but nevertheless causes an important increase in drag.

Research engineers found that very smooth surfaces helped to keep laminar flow from becoming turbulent. The "flush" rivet was developed to eliminate the rounded head of the ordinary rivet. The flush rivet fits into a dimple in the metal skin, and the top surface of the rivet can be finished off smooth and flush. But even on the smoothest wing that could be built, the flow still tripped up and became turbulent after traveling less than one-fifth of the distance from the leading edge to the trailing edge.

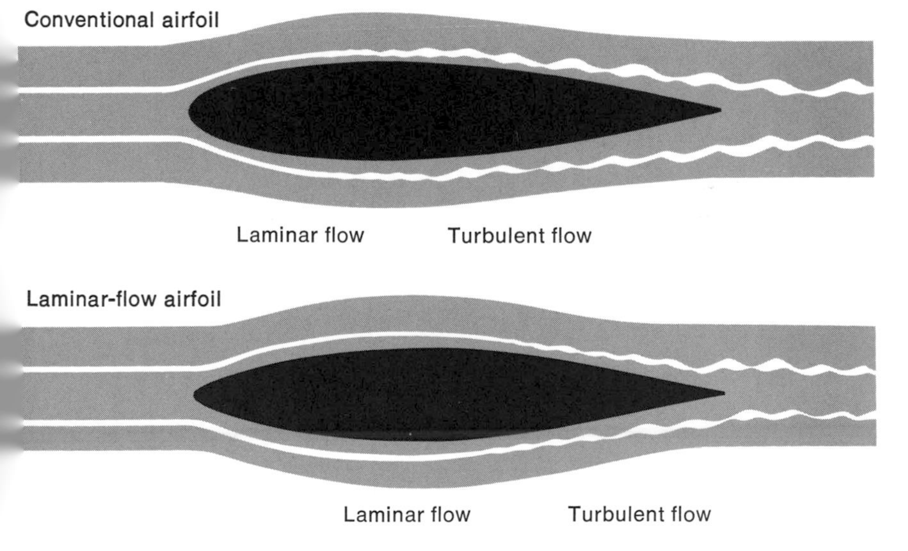

5.4 The special shape of the laminar-flow airfoil may make possible low-drag airflow over more than half of a wing.

NACA researchers found that by giving the airfoil a special shape, the low-drag flow might be continued over more of the wing. The so-called laminar-flow airfoil is not greatly different from an ordinary airfoil, but if you look closely you can see that it reaches its maximum thickness farther back — perhaps near the midpoint of the airfoil (figure 5.4). The steadily increasing thickness over the front half of the airfoil causes the air to steadily increase its speed as it flows over this area. This little trick keeps the laminar boundary layer from growing so tired that it trips and becomes turbulent. Airfoils of this type are used on most airplanes today.

After the air flows past the region of maximum thickness of the wing, nothing can keep the boundary layer from becoming turbulent. Nothing, that is, except removing the boundary layer itself. Engineers found that by carefully drawing off this tired layer of air through porous surfaces, holes, or slots in the wing surface, low-drag laminar flow might be continued over still more of the wing. Unfortunately, the power required and the weight of the pumps and piping needed for a "boundary-layer suction" system tend to cancel the advantages. Of the few airplanes constructed with this feature, most have been for experimental purposes.

The invention of the turbojet engine made possible a great spurt in airplane speeds. Because airplanes were approaching the speed of sound, streamlining became even more important. In order to delay the sonic problems, wings were made thinner and sharper. Short stubby wings, arrow shaped "delta" wings, and slender, flexible swept-back wings all moved in to replace the usual low-speed shapes.

While some engineers struggled with the problems of making an airplane fly as fast as possible, others were working just as hard on the problem of making an airplane fly as *slowly* as possible. A slow landing speed is desirable for any airplane. Also, because an airplane must be flown near the ground for landing and takeoff, it should be easy and safe to fly at low speeds, with no tricky characteristics or sudden surprises to spoil the pilot's day.

Wing flaps were developed to help the wing support the airplane at a much lower speed. You can look at a lowered wing flap and tell what it does — it gives the air passing over the wing an extra push downward to produce more lift on the wing. With more lift, the airplane can remain in the air at a lower speed than before. The flap also increases the drag of the airplane, as you might expect. Increased drag and increased lift are both helpful on the landing approach because the airplane can descend more steeply and touch down at a lower speed.

To permit the airplane to fly safely at slow speeds where angle of attack must be large, special devices were developed for the leading edge of the wing. These devices, such as fixed "slots" or retractable "slats," guide high-pressure air from beneath the wing around or through the wing leading edge to the top of the wing (figure 5.5). Here this air with its extra energy can sweep down over the top surface to help keep the flow from stalling at high angles of attack.

These powerful flaps, wing slats, and other low-speed features led to the design of a special kind of airplane that can take off and land at very slow speeds. Called *STOL* aircraft, for Short TakeOff and Landing, these machines have been very useful for short jungle airstrips, rough battlefield airstrips, or short landing fields surrounded by high obstructions. Small STOL transports are used to carry passengers from main air terminals to downtown airports or outlying fields that have short runways.

5.5 Helio STOL in flight. Slats at the wing leading edge and large flaps at the trailing edge help this STOL airplane to give the airstream a greater downward deflection; hence it can fly at very low speed. COURTESY OF HELIO AIRCRAFT

Another strange group of aircraft is the *VTOL,* or Vertical TakeOff and Landing craft. The helicopter is one type of VTOL with which we are all familiar. The helicopter can take off vertically because it develops its lift by means of spinning rotor blades rather than through forward motion of a wing. Other types of VTOL aircraft have wings for horizontal flight, but must blast air downward with their propulsion systems in order to lift off the ground before moving into horizontal flight. This requirement makes VTOL airplanes complicated and often strange-looking vehicles.

Several jet-propelled VTOL airplanes (figure 5.6) have been built using powerful, lightweight turbojet engines with movable vanes in the jet exhaust. Deflected downward, the jet exhaust provides the lift to take off, hover, or land with no forward motion. As the vanes are moved slowly to turn the jet rearward, some of the lift force becomes thrust and the airplane begins to move horizontally. The wings begin to take over the job of providing lift, and when the jet exhaust reaches the horizontal position, it provides only thrust, with the wing providing all of the lift.

Other interesting VTOL airplanes have been built in which the engine and propeller can be tilted along with the wing to the vertical position for takeoff and slowly rotated to the horizontal position for level flight (figure 5.7). Another propeller-driven machine was designed to stand on its tail and take off vertically, like a rocket. In order to land again, the pilot swooped into a vertical position and throttled his engine to ease the airplane tail first down to the ground. The landing turned out to be a difficult maneuver indeed, because the pilot had to fly the airplane backward with great precision while looking over his shoulder! A similar jet-powered airplane was built to use only a piece of steel cable stretched between two poles for an airport. After swooping to the vertical position, the pilot extended a hook from the nose of the fuselage and maneuvered the airplane to hang it on the cable.

5.6 This jet-propelled VTOL airplane can hover like a hummingbird by deflecting its jet exhaust downward by means of special turning vanes and ducts.

COURTESY OF BELL AEROSYSTEMS COMPANY

Such machines must have a great deal of power for their weight, but like the helicopter, they have the advantage of being able to land almost anywhere. Thus far, the helicopter is the only VTOL that has been widely used, but we can expect to see some interesting STOL and VTOL airplanes in the future.

The steady progress in aeronautics has given us not only faster airplanes, but a great variety of airplanes that can do very special things. The job of the earliest airplanes was simple: to get off the ground and fly, somehow. The job of the modern airplane is very definite and has been all picked out before the vehicle is designed. Each airplane is a compromise, designed to do certain things well at the cost of most others.

The helicopter is a good example of compromise. It's number one requirement is to be able to land anywhere — even in your own backyard. In order to do this, it needs a huge rotor and a great deal of power. Compared with other aircraft, the helicopter is expensive, slow, and has a small payload and a short range. But these things are the price that must be paid for the ability to land anywhere.

The jet transport has a very different special purpose. It carries passengers for a great distance at high speed, but it requires an airport with vast concrete runways for takeoff and landing.

The supersonic fighter is again different. It is designed to travel at twice the speed of sound, but it can do so for only a very short distance, and it cannot carry passengers or land in anyone's backyard.

The small private airplane is a very versatile vehicle. It is designed to be easy to fly, to operate economically, to land at big airports or small, and to provide comfortable transporta-

5.7 This propeller-driven VTOL airplane can take off and land vertically, using propellers to produce the lifting force.

COURTESY OF VOUGHT AERONAUTICS DIVISION, LTV AEROSPACE CORPORATION

tion. But it, too, is a compromise — it cannot perform the special feats of the helicopter, jet transport, or supersonic fighter.

Because airplanes can perform a great variety of jobs, the number of airplanes in the United States has skyrocketed, doubling in the past five years and promising to double again in the next five. Today's civil air fleet consists of two main categories: public transporation — the airlines — and general aviation — all the other private and business airplanes. Together these two fleets have made the United States the most aeronautical nation on earth. Many people envision the first group as a vast fleet of transports, the second group as a small number of miscellaneous aircraft. Surprisingly enough, it's not that way at all. The airline fleet of the United States operates over 2,000 aircraft, but for every transport airplane, there are more than sixty general-aviation airplanes. During a typical recent year, the airlines of the United States carried over 13 million passengers to foreign countries and over 118 million between terminals within the United States, but as many people used general aviation's fleet of over 120,000 aircraft as were carried as passengers on all the airlines combined. About one third of all the people traveling by air between cities were carried by general aviation. We can expect rapid growth in the future for the airlines, but even faster growth for general aviation. The airlines will add 1,000 transports over the next ten years, but general aviation is expected to add over 100,000 airplanes to its fleet.

Aviation began as a private venture, and privately owned airplanes continue to be the fastest-growing group in aviation. In the next few chapters we will look at the private airplane, its equipment, and how it is flown.

6

The Private Airplane

"OKAY, OPEN THE THROTTLE and let's go."

Very slowly the airplane began to move across the grass. After what seemed like quite a while, the instructor motioned for me to move the stick back. With its 40-horsepower engine straining up front, the airplane lifted off and climbed, oh so slowly, toward the telephone wires at the edge of the airport. At 1,000 feet over neatly checkered Indiana farmland the instructor began my first flying lesson.

We sat one behind the other in the tiny cabin beneath the wing. Because the student must fly this airplane from the rear seat to balance the airplane properly when flying solo, the instructor sat in the front seat. The student had to look over the instructor's shoulder to see the instrument panel or the sky ahead, and the instructor had to turn around to yell at his student.

After nearly an hour of maneuvers, the instructor motioned us back to the field, where he used hand signals to direct the landing. We touched down smoothly, and rolled to a stop. I've never been sure which one of us made that landing, but with that airplane nobody had to do very much.

The airplane was a Piper Cub, the first really successful private airplane and the great-grandfather of the airplane I would own many years later.

Strictly speaking, the Cub was not the first private airplane or even the first airplane designed for sport flying. After all, the Wright Brothers began their gliding experiments purely as a sport, and had hardly more serious ideas when they developed the first airplane. Much of the early flying in America and the rest of the world was done for adventure, for the sport of it.

Most private airplanes on the scene when the Cub arrived were large machines with large engines. Because the science of aerodynamics had not yet solved all of its problems, many of these airplanes, especially the ones designed for high performance, tended to have tricky characteristics.

But the Cub, and others like it, presented a new idea. Not designed for daredevil pilots, wealthy sportsmen, or professional pilots, but rather for the general public, they were simple, inexpensive, and easy to fly. They were also small, underpowered, and slow. The Cub was called the "flivver of the air," after Henry Ford's "flivver," the famous Model T Ford. The budding lightplane industry began to talk of "a plane in every garage." The day of a car in every garage had almost arrived — why not a plane next?

Because airplanes were largely handmade, dozens of manufacturers popped up to turn out a few dozen or a few hundred airplanes. Most of the names of these firms, like those of the builders of early motor cars, have disappeared from the private airplane market — names like Porterfield, Funk, Taylor, Monocoupe, Fairchild, Fleet, Rearwin, Aeronca, and Stinson, to name a few.

Only a handful of the companies active in the 1920's, 1930's and 1940's are still in business, and they have become the giants of the industry.

The Cub was a remarkable design for its day, though its construction was conventional. The fuselage was welded steel tubing, fabric covered, its wing wood and metal, also fabric covered. The tiny air-cooled engine up front developed about 40 horsepower and turned a laminated-wood propeller. The airplane had no brakes. It landed at less than 40 miles per hour anyway, and soon came to a stop with its tailskid — a flat spring of metal that supported the tail — dragging in the grass. Its cruising speed was less than 70 miles per hour, and it carried enough fuel for only a couple of hundred miles of flight. It could be bought for less than $1,400.

The most remarkable feature of the Cub was its flying qualities. It was gentle and easy to fly. It stalled gently, and only when forced to do so. It would spin, but only when forced, and would recover by itself if the controls were released. These features made it a good trainer, and thousands of pilots learned to fly in the Cub and its descendants. More than three-quarters of all pilots trained for World War II received their basic training in Cubs, and many of today's jet-airliner pilots started their aviation careers in Cubs.

A few lessons were all I got in the Cub, and it was some years later when I set out in earnest to learn to fly. The airplane in which I found myself was a direct descendant of the Cub. Called the Piper Cruiser, it had 90 horsepower — more than twice that of the Cub. The pilot sat up front, and the rear seat was designed for two people, if they didn't mind being a little crowded.

We had been shooting landings for two or three lessons and things seemed to be going especially well one day. As we taxied back for another takeoff, the instructor said, "Stop here for a moment." He swung open the door, unbuckled his seat belt, and began to climb out.

"Where are you going?" I had already guessed, but couldn't quite believe it.

"It's time you flew this thing by yourself," he said. "Make three landings and then come back to the hangar."

No pilot ever forgets his first solo flight — the airplane, his thoughts, those first landings. I took a long look at the empty seat behind me as the airplane climbed out of the field, and I was exhilarated at the thought of being up there alone. After one bouncy landing and two good ones, I taxied back to the hangar. While someone was handing me a cold bottle of pop, someone else hacked off the tail of my shirt, as is the custom with newly-soloed students.

During the late 1940's the light-airplane industry slipped into a severe depression. Somehow the demand for an airplane in every garage had not materialized, and many small airplane companies simply went out of business. The survivors recognized that there was a specific need for the private airplane as a fast means of transportation for people who needed to travel. They began to build airplanes having higher performance, longer range, and more seats (figures 6.1, 6.2, and 6.3).

All-metal airplanes began to appear, and soon largely replaced tube-and-fabric models except for training and agricultural airplanes. Tricycle landing gear, which had been so

6.1 a The Piper Cub

6.1 b Piper Cherokee

COURTESY OF PIPER AIRCRAFT CORPORATION

6.2 a An early Beech model

6.2 b A modern Beech Bonanza
COURTESY OF BEECH AIRCRAFT CORPORATION

6.3 a Clyde Cessna in his 1912 *Silver Wings*

6.3 b 1 A modern Cessna Skyhawk

6.3 b 2 Cessna light twin

COURTESY OF CESSNA AIRCRAFT COMPANY

successful on large military and transport aircraft, made airplanes more comfortable and easier to handle on the ground. Faster airplanes were equipped with retractable landing gear.

Flat or *horizontally-opposed* engines were developed in larger and larger sizes. This type of engine, which had been developed in very small sizes for early light airplanes, has its cylinders (two, four, or six, depending upon the engine horsepower) mounted horizontally (figure 6.4). This engine eliminated the need for the huge nose and cowling required by the radial engine. The flat engine made possible a smaller, more streamlined nose, with better visibility for the pilot and better performance for the airplane.

Expanding instrument panels and new navigation aids made long-distance travel by personal airplane more and more attractive. "Light twins" began to find a market with the private owner who needed more than one engine, more speed, or more range. Among the twins and the larger singles, six-passenger models were produced for larger families and for the growing charter and air-taxi business.

The modern private airplane, which we will use for familiarization here and for illustration in later chapters on flying, is a sleek, beautiful machine. Built stronger than an airliner, with an engine so reliable that engine failures are very rare, the airplane itself is a very safe vehicle. In the hands of a well-trained pilot who understands his airplane and exercises good judgment in its operation, it can be a very safe, comfortable, fast means of transportation.

Most airplanes today are built with aerodynamic characteristics that make them docile and easy to fly. The great danger of early airplanes was the *stall.* If flown at too slow a speed, these airplanes could stall suddenly and roll off on one wing into a "spin." The spin is an aggravated stall in which the airplane turns in a tight spiral path and loses altitude rapidly. The stall-spin was long a primary cause of airplane accidents during landing and takeoff. But the wings of today's airplanes are designed to stall gradually. A built-in twist gives the wing tips a lower angle of attack, so the center sections (near the fuselage) reach the angle of stall first (figure 6.5). The airplane warns the pilot that the wing is beginning to stall by shaking and rumbling and losing lift. Meanwhile, the outer

6.4 Six-cylinder light-airplane engine, showing horizontal arrangement of the cylinders COURTESY OF BEECH AIRCRAFT CORPORATION

part of the wing where the ailerons are located is still unstalled and keeps the airplane flying and controllable.

Because of their improved aerodynamics, most of today's light airplanes will spin only if forced to; some will not spin at all. In the days of the Cub, a pilot was required in his flight test to show that he could do a spin and a spin recovery. Because so many airplanes are now spinproof, this maneuver is no

6.5a Small pieces of yarn taped to upper surface of the wing show smooth flow in normal level flight. As wing begins to stall (6.5b), yarn points the directions of the rough separated airflow over the inboard half of the wing. Because the wing is designed with a smaller angle of attack toward the tip, the outboard half of the wing has unstalled flow.

COURTESY OF BEECH AIRCRAFT CORPORATION

longer required. But the stall, even in its milder forms, still is a hazard near the ground. Because the pilot must perform the landing approach at low speed, and must closely approach the stall at the point of touchdown, he must be able to fly the airplane safely at low speeds and stall it only when he intends to do so.

Most light airplanes are designed so that large control forces

6.5 b COURTESY OF BEECH AIRCRAFT CORPORATION

and motions are required to reach the stall. Because he must exert a large force and a large movement, the pilot is not likely to get himself into this condition except when he wishes to do so. Most airplanes are also equipped with a *stall-warning indicator* that flashes a red light on the panel or sounds a warning when the airplane nears the stalled condition.

The cabin of the modern private plane is spacious and wide,

with comfortable, adjustable seats and large windows. Cabin heat and ventilation are provided, and some airplanes even have air conditioners. Usually, however, you can provide your own air conditioning by flying in the cool, dry air at high altitudes.

Not all private airplanes are built in factories. As mentioned previously, most early airplanes could probably be considered "home-built" or "amateur-built." Today many interesting, attractive little planes are built in sheds, garages, basements, or even living rooms by amateur craftsmen.

Aircraft construction by amateurs got its start after World War I, when many people were excited enough about aviation to attempt to build their own airplanes. Because the science of aerodynamics was not yet well developed, and because many amateurs lacked the high level of skill needed to build an airplane, some of these projects produced poor results and even disastrous crashes. In the early 1930's the federal government cracked down hard on home-built planes and almost brought amateur building to a stop. Some hardy pioneers who could satisfy the complicated requirements and red tape of the government aviation agency continued to build and fly their own planes.

After World War II a great many people turned again to building their own planes, and in the early 1950's, a group of successful, competent amateur builders formed the Experimental Aircraft Association to promote home building as a hobby. Over a period of years, the Federal Aviation Agency became convined that under proper supervision and with proper standards, home building could be an appealing and satisfying hobby and could produce a safe, useful product. There are now over forty thousand members of this Association, and at least three thousand home-built airplanes are flying in the United States, with several thousand more under construction. Some amateur builders design their own, others rely upon plans which can be obtained from professional designers. Nearly all use factory-built engines, propellers, instruments, wheels, and fittings, but the airframes themselves are built by hand. Designs vary from fetching little miniature biplanes to sleek miniature racing craft that look like tiny fighter airplanes (figure 6.6). Even amphibians and autogyros pop up now and then. Most home-builts are sport airplanes, although some high-performance cross-country airplanes and even a few twin-engined ships are being built.

Many home-builts are made of the traditional steel tubing, wood, and fabric; others may be all-wood or all-metal. Some projects take as much as several years of hard work to complete, but on completion the pilot-builder has the supreme experience of taking to the air in something that he has created with his own hands.

Another very special kind of private aircraft is built with one important part missing — the engine. But in the hands of a skilled pilot, the *glider* needs no engine. On silent wings, it can travel hundreds of miles, remain in the air for hours, and soar to altitudes of several miles, using only the power of the atmosphere. There is no new principle of flight involved here, and no magic — just a combination of sophisticated aerodynamic design and very skillful piloting. The glider is designed and built so efficiently that it glides at a very flat angle, losing altitude very slowly as it travels. The pilot's job is to find air that is moving *upward* faster than he is gliding *downward*. As

6.6 a The Stolp Starduster
COURTESY OF MIKE FREY

Thousands of sport airplanes have been built by amateur craftsmen.

6.6 b The Bushby Mustang II
COURTESY OF EXPERIMENTAL AIRCRAFT ASSOCIATION

long as he can find this air and use it properly, the sky is his. When no upward-moving air is available, he must quickly choose a landing site within his gliding range.

The sport of gliding and soaring was started on a large scale in Germany in 1920 and soon spread to the rest of the world. At first the up-slope winds on the windward side of hills and mountain ridges were used to keep gliders aloft, but later when "thermals" were discovered, gliding and soaring moved out into any type of terrain where the sun shines.

We can look at a high-performance glider (sometimes called a "sailplane") and recognize some of the features that give it a high degree of aerodynamic efficiency (figure 6.7). Its surfaces are smooth and highly polished to reduce friction drag. Its wing section and the shape of all components are carefully engineered for optimum performance. And most important, it has a huge wing span to reduce to a minimum that inescapable bugaboo of all heavier-than-air machines — drag due to lift. The extremely long, tapered, flexible wings of the modern glider may give it a lift-to-drag ratio of 40 or more. This number means that one pound of lift "costs" only 1/40 pound of thrust to produce. To put it in a way more useful to the glider pilot, an L/D of 40 means that one mile of altitude will permit a glide of 40 miles in still air. In sharp contrast with these very efficient machines, the average light airplane may have an L/D of 10 or less, and a large, clean, high-speed jet transport about 17.

For training flights, the glider may be pulled into the air by an automobile or by a winch on the ground. For soaring flights it is often towed aloft by an airplane to an altitude of 2,000 feet or more, where the glider pilot has greater opportunity to find thermals to keep him aloft. Releasing his silent craft from the towrope, the pilot seeks the vertical updrafts that form over sun-heated terrain. These thermals are columns or bubbles of warm air rising in a cooler atmosphere. The puffy white cumulus "fair weather" clouds usually mark the tops of these

6.7 Glider in flight

COURTESY OF ROBERT LEE MOORE

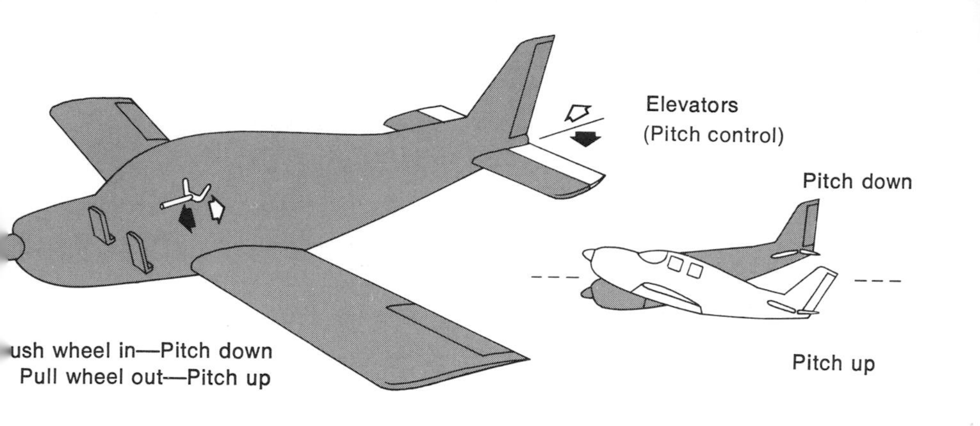

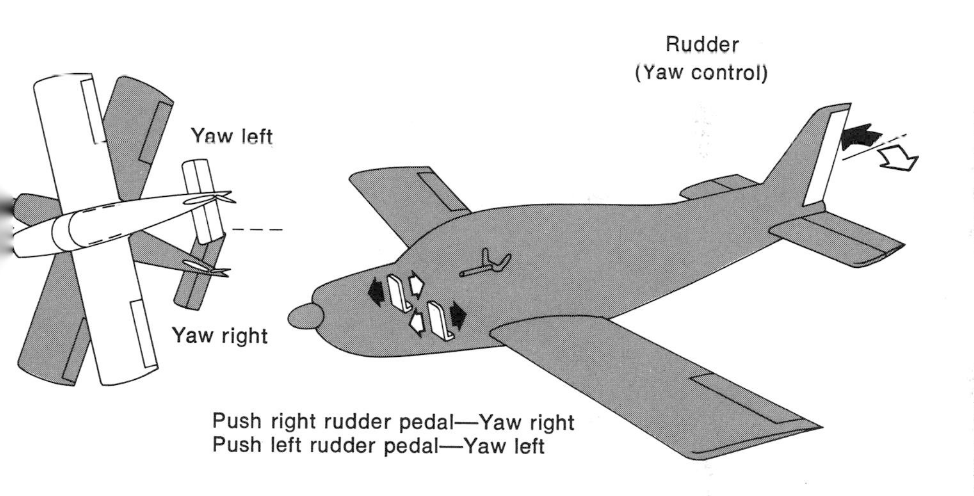

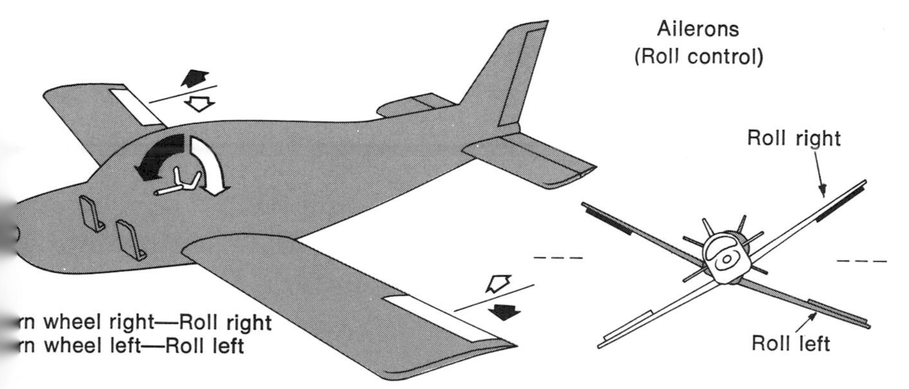

6.8 The pilot's controls and the airplane's aerodynamic-control surfaces

bubbles. By circling his machine at low speed in a thermal, the pilot can gain altitude until the top of the bubble is reached. He can then glide in any direction he wishes, losing altitude slowly, gaining it back again in the next thermal he can find. By this process, sailplanes can travel hundreds of miles, sometimes at average speeds of over 60 miles per hour, coming back to earth only when the thermals weaken and disappear in the late afternoon. The world distance record for gliders is (at this writing) 647 miles — started with a tow to an altitude of 2,000 feet and powered only by the atmosphere from that point.

Ridge soaring is like surfing in reverse. The tremendous wave of air that forms as the wind rides over a ridge of hills or mountains provides the up-current to carry the glider to great heights. The world altitude record for gliders — 46,000 feet — was reached with this kind of soaring.

Gliding has become an established sport that has great appeal to the beginner as well as the experienced pilot. Because he depends upon nothing but his own skill to keep his machine aloft, the glider pilot perhaps comes closest to achieving man's old dream of imitating the birds.

For all heavier-than-air machines, regardless of their uses or purposes, the aerodynamic control surfaces and the pilot's controls that operate them are much the same (figure 6.8). These are the "tools" of the pilot, with which the student must be adequately familiar before he begins to fly. The airplane instrument panel holds dozens of other "tools"; an array of dials, switches, and equipment that looks bewildering at first glance. As we examine most of these instruments one by one in the next chapter, they will lose their mystery and become friendly little faces that give us vital information we need while we fly.

7

Dials, Switches, and Black Boxes

A PHOTOGRAPH OF A PILOT ready to make an attempt to fly in 1903 shows a barometer strapped to his knee, presumably to tell him his altitude (figure 7.1). This photograph records the first recognition of the fact that pilots would need instruments to help them in their work. But in this particular case the pilot was optimistic about his need for a barometer. When his craft, S. P. Langley's "Aerodrome," was catapulted from the launching platform, it fell into the river.

Most of the very early airplanes used no instruments at all, except perhaps for an engine tachometer to show engine speed. Even on early "long-distance" flights, such as the first crossing of the English Channel, the pilot did not carry even a compass. But it was soon recognized that the pilot needed to know certain things about his engine, his airplane, and his flight. Within about twenty years the airplane instrument panel had accumulated over a dozen instruments and controls. In some airplanes the instruments gave the pilot enough information

7.1 Samuel P. Langley's pilot for two attempted launchings of the Aerodrome was his assistant, Charles M. Manley. Note the barometer fastened to his knee.
COURTESY OF NATIONAL AIR AND SPACE MUSEUM, SMITHSONIAN INSTITUTION

to enable him to fly entirely by reference to his instruments. Charles A. Lindbergh, on his transatlantic flight in 1927, had no radio and only eleven instruments on the panel of *The Spirit of St. Louis* (figure 7.2). Yet he flew 3,600 miles through daylight and dark, through fog and storm and found his way, as planned, from New York to Paris.

The modern light training airplane has several dozen dials, switches, and controls on its panel, while the well-equipped private airplane may have fifty or more, and the multi-engine jet, many hundreds. The instruments, communication equipment, and navigation gear are vital to the operation of the airplane, and the pilot must understand how they operate and must know how to use them.

The engine gauges are usually located in one group on a lightplane panel (figure 7.3). We are all accustomed to seeing oil pressure, generator output, fuel quantity, and cooling-water temperature displayed in some way on our automobile dashboard. An airplane panel will have these same items, but with oil temperature instead of water temperature because the air-

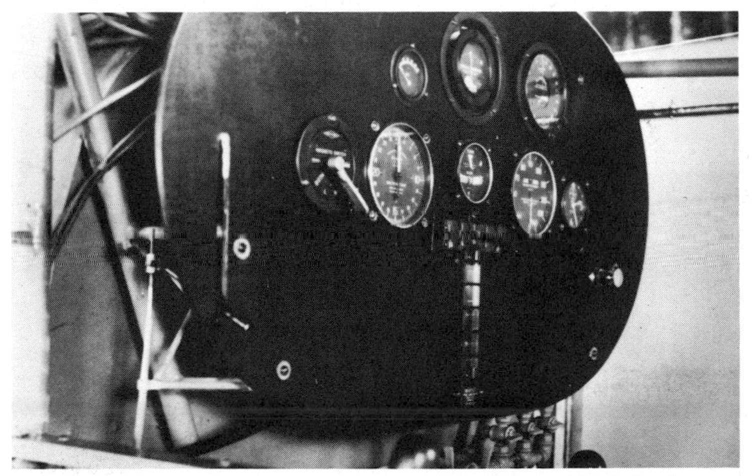

7.2 The instrument panel of *The Spirit of St. Louis* in which Lindbergh flew the Atlantic from New York to Paris in 1927
COURTESY OF NATIONAL AIR AND SPACE MUSEUM, SMITHSONIAN INSTITUTION

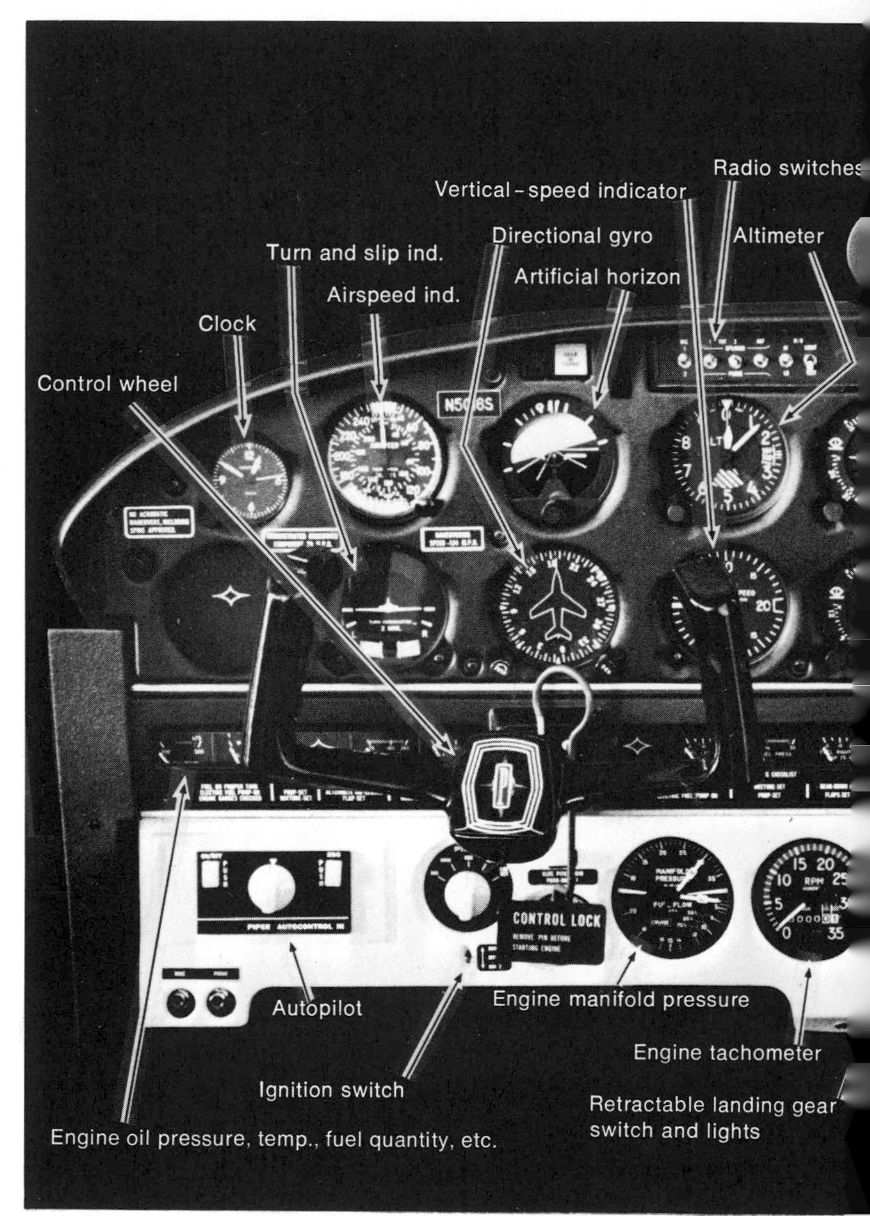

7.3 The instrument panel of a typical well-equipped light airplane

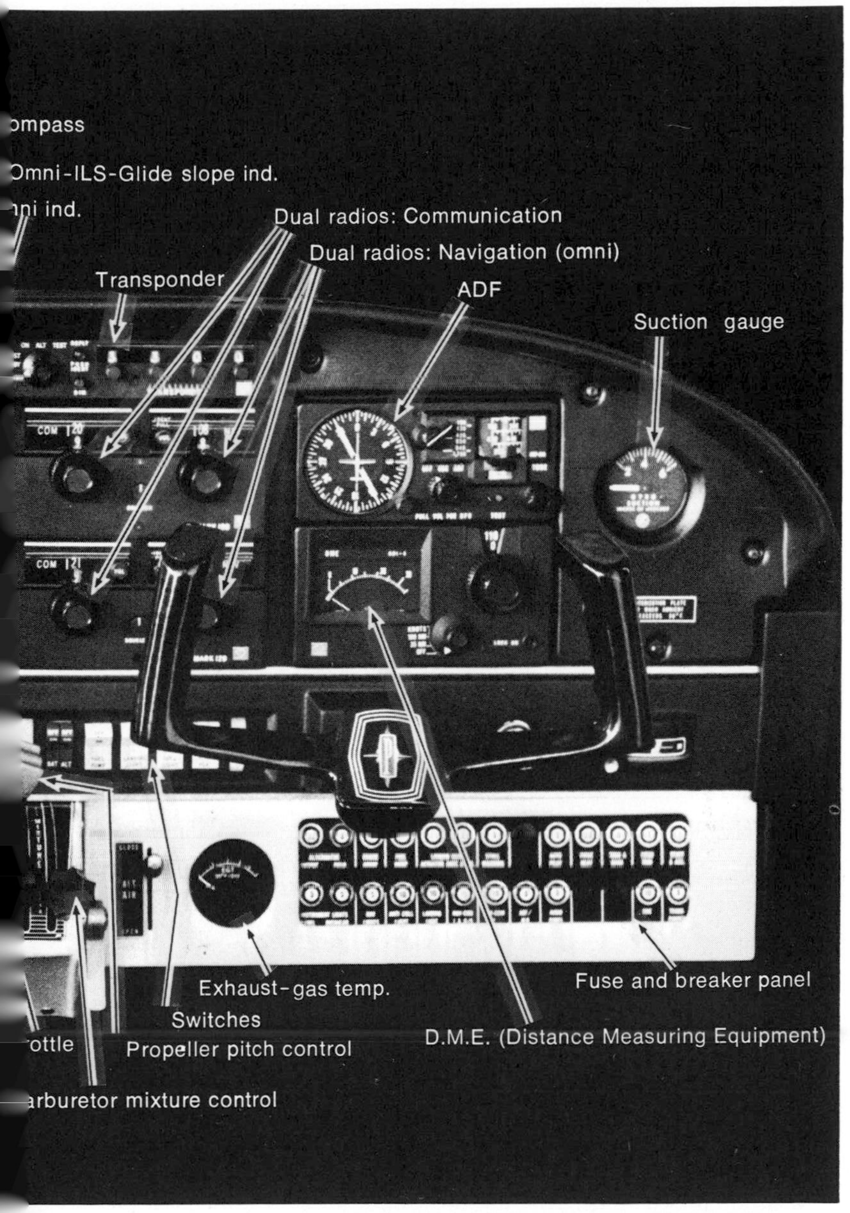

COURTESY OF PIPER AIRCRAFT CORPORATION

plane engine has no cooling water. There is also a tachometer for indicating engine speed in revolutions per minute (RPM). This instrument is not found on cars except for some sports cars and foreign models. More complex airplanes may have indicators for exhaust-gas temperature, cylinder-head temperature, carburetor temperature, and carburetor air-intake pressure. All of these items help the pilot to know what is going on in his engine so that he may control it more accurately and spot trouble before it becomes important.

The main engine control is the *throttle* — a knob or lever usually near the center of the panel in airplanes where pilot and copilot sit side by side. Pushing the control all the way forward opens the throttle for full engine power. If the airplane has a fixed-pitch propeller, the pilot selects the amount of power he wants by adjusting the speed of the engine with the throttle. If the airplane has a variable-pitch propeller, another knob or lever is located on the panel near the throttle to control the propeller. On this kind of airplane, the engine speed depends upon the propeller setting; consequently, the pilot must adjust both the propeller and the throttle to select the amount of engine power he wants. The pilot will normally take off and climb with the propeller in "flat pitch." After reaching cruising altitude, he throttles back the engine and moves the propeller blades to high pitch to increase their "bite" at high speeds.

Another engine control is the *carburetor mixture control.* Because the airplane operates at all sorts of altitudes, the pilot needs a control with which he can adjust the fuel flow to the carburetor to match the air density. If we attempted to take off with a sea-level mixture from an airport at a 7,000-foot altitude in Wyoming, the engine would literally choke on excessive fuel, and might not even develop enough power to get off the ground. But with the fuel-air mixture "leaned out" for the thin air at that altitude, the same airplane can fly efficiently at an altitude of two miles, or even higher, though it will, of course, deliver less power than it would in the denser sea-level air.

The carburetor of an automobile is adjusted for the altitude where it is usually operated. A car adjusted for the altitude of Los Angeles will run very poorly and seem to have little power on a mountain road in the High Sierras. It is choking on too much fuel. If the automobile had a mixture control (which it ordinarily does not have), the engine fuel-air mixture could be adjusted to give better performance at different altitudes.

The ignition switch on an airplane is different from that on a car, and for good reason. As a safety feature, the airplane has two separate ignition systems, including two spark plugs in each cylinder. The ignition switch will have four positions: off, left, right, both. Normally run on "both," the ignition can be switched first to the "right" system and then the "left" system before takeoff to check for proper operation of each system.

Another engine control peculiar to the airplane is the *carburetor heat lever*. When engine air shoots through the narrow "throat" of the carburetor, it drops in pressure. The temperature of the air also drops, and might drop to below freezing even on a warm day. When the air is humid, ice can form in the carburetor, particularly when the engine power is reduced for landing, and stop the engine. When the pilot suspects that ice may be forming, he moves his carburetor heat lever to send engine air through a heater on its way to the carburetor. The heated air is less likely to deposit ice in the carburetor.

Many automobile drivers pay so little attention to their engine instruments that they fail to see warnings such as high engine temperature or low oil pressure. Some manufacturers have replaced indicators with red warning lights with the idea that drivers may be more likely to notice a red light than a pointer on a dial. But an airplane pilot must pay close attention to his engine, because trouble there may mean an emergency landing. He checks engine operation very carefully before takeoff and examines his instruments frequently in flight in order to control his engine accurately and to spot trouble before it becomes serious.

The instruments that the pilot uses to help him control the airplane itself are called *flight instruments.* There are three that he will always find on the panel in front of him, for they are required by federal regulations. They are the *compass,* the *airspeed indicator,* and the *altimeter.* Most airplanes will also have a *turn-and-slip indicator,* sometimes called the *turn-and-bank indicator.* Although there may be many more, these are the instruments that a student pilot will need and use in his early flight training.

The compass most often used in lightplanes consists of a magnet mounted on a small cylinder that floats in a glass container of liquid (figure 7.4). The magnet aligns itself with the magnetic field of the earth, like the needle of a Boy Scout compass, to point at the magnetic north pole. The floating cylinder is marked off in degrees. The case of the instrument turns with the airplane, and the markings tell the pilot what angle (from magnetic north) his airplane is pointing. A compass reading of 0° means that the airplane is pointing north; 90° means that the airplane is pointing east (and is shown as "E" on the cylinder); 180° means south, and 270° means west. For most

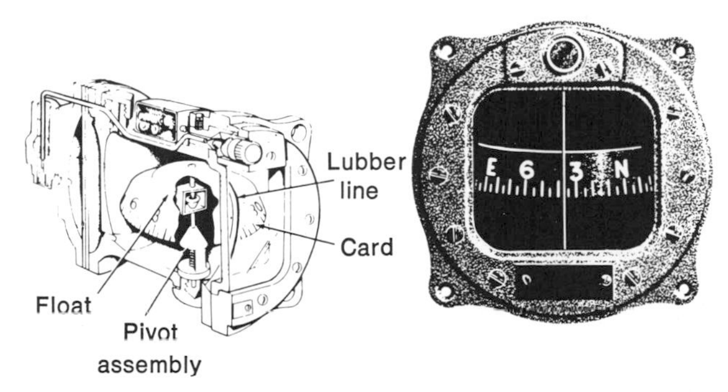

7.4 The magnetic compass

of the seven hundred years since its invention the compass has been the principal tool of the maritime navigator. It is still a basic tool in aeronautical navigation today.

Many of the flight instruments on the airplane's panel do not measure directly what they indicate on their dials. The altimeter (figure 7.5) is one of these. It does not measure altitude at all but measures instead an *air pressure*. The earth's atmosphere is an ocean of air that is held to the earth's surface by the force of gravity. The air presses down upon the earth's surface, and us, with a pressure of almost 15 pounds per square inch at sea level. At higher altitudes this pressure decreases because there is less air above pressing down. We can think of the altimeter as simply a kind of barometer for measuring this pressure to tell us how "deep" we are in the earth's atmosphere. The altimeter has an air-tight case, and contains a small metal box or "diaphragm" that has been evacuated so that there is (almost) zero air pressure inside. The pressure piped into the instrument case is the "static" pressure of the atmosphere. It is taken from a small hole in the side of the fuselage or from holes drilled in the side of the airplane's *pitot-*

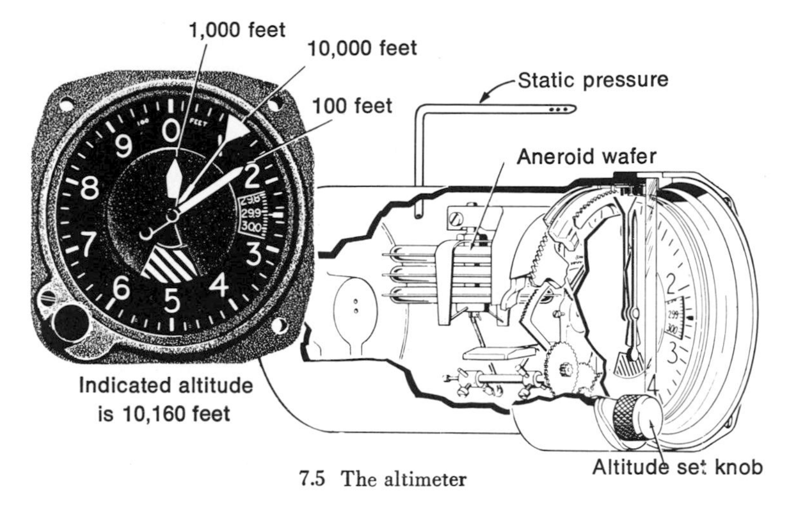

7.5 The altimeter

COURTESY OF FEDERAL AVIATION AGENCY

static head which is mounted in the airstream, usually under the wing. This pressure depends only upon altitude and is unaffected by motion of the airplane. The pressure squeezes the diaphragm into a flatter shape at sea level and lets it expand at higher altitudes. This motion is geared to the indicator hands, which point to a scale calibrated in feet of altitude. Most altimeters have three hands that operate much like the hands of a clock. The large hand indicates hundreds of feet, while a smaller one indicates thousands and a third shows tens of thousands.

Because the pressure of the atmosphere changes day by day and from one place to another, we must correct the altimeter for these changes. All pilots keep their altimeters set to the equivalent sea-level barometric pressure using the knob and the window on the right side of the instrument face. Everybody's altimeter then reads actual altitude *above sea level* (think of it as an imaginary sea level if you are far from the ocean) for that time and place, not altitude above the ground.

If you land at an airport that is 3,000 feet above sea level, your altimeter will read "3000" when you are on the ground.

The airspeed indicator (figure 7.6) is another instrument

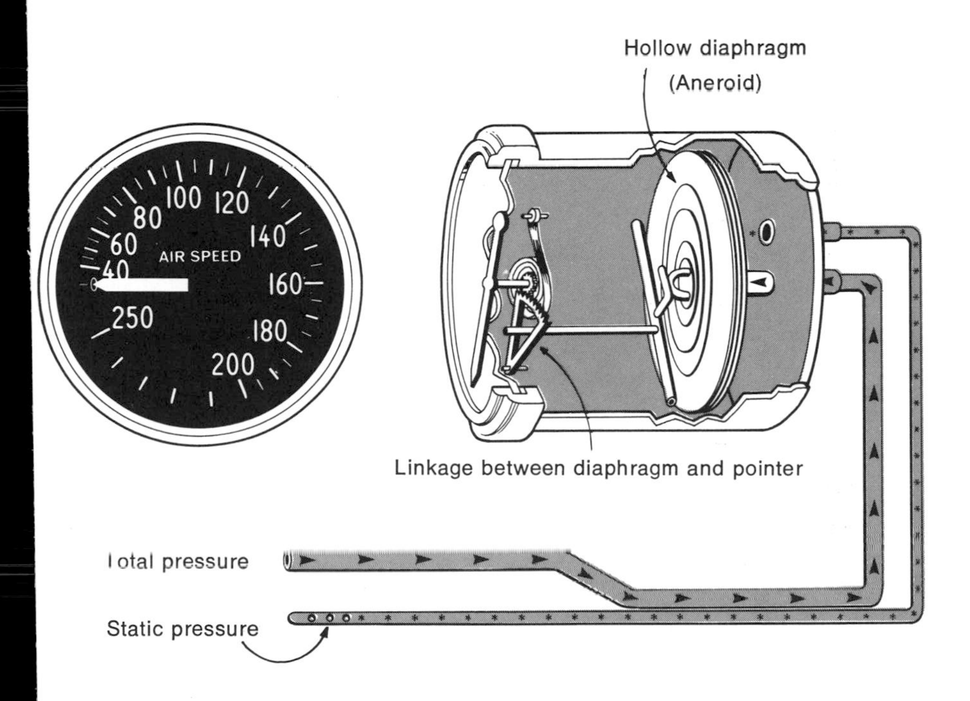

7.6 The airspeed indicator

that does not make its measurement directly. It does not really measure airspeed, but measures instead a *pressure* that depends upon airspeed. The instrument is like an altimeter, with a thin, flexible metal box or diaphragm mounted in an airtight case. But in this instrument the diaphragm is not evacuated. A small pipe or tube from the pitot-static head brings static pressure to the inside of the sealed instrument case. This pressure, as we said earlier, depends only upon altitude and is unaffected by motion of the airplane. A second pressure, called *total pressure,* is brought to the inside of the diaphragm. Impact pressure is taken from the opening in the *end* of the pitot head that points forward into the oncoming air, and is the pressure that you feel when you extend your hand from a cockpit or a car window flat against the airstream. This pressure depends upon the speed of the airplane — the higher the speed, the greater the pressure. The diaphragm thus "feels" the difference between total and static pressure, a difference which is due solely to *speed*. The larger pressure inside the diaphragm causes it to expand as the speed increases. This movement is connected through gears to the hand of the indicator, which points to a scale calibrated in either miles per hour or knots (nautical miles per hour).

The turn-and-slip indicator really gives us two instruments in the same case (figure 7.7). The turn indicator is a gyroscopic device that will be described more fully in a later chapter. We can say here that a spinning gyroscope wheel resists being turned and deflects the needle to tell the pilot when his airplane is turning and how rapidly. The slip indicator is by far the simplest of all the instruments on the panel. It's just a steel ball in a curved tube of oil. When the airplane is flying level or in a properly banked turn, the ball stays centered in the tube. But when the pilot skids or slips the airplane, the ball rolls off center in the direction of the skid, warning the pilot of this condition.

The well-equipped trainer or a cross-country airplane may have another group of flight instruments called the *instrument-flight group,* which will be discussed in Chapter 10.

In the days of automatic this-and-that, we should not be surprised to find an *automatic pilot* on the panel of many airplanes. The autopilot does just what the pilot does — takes information from the airplane's instruments and moves the

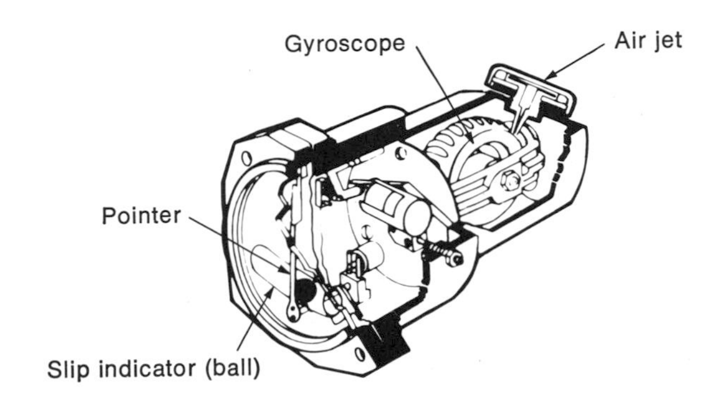

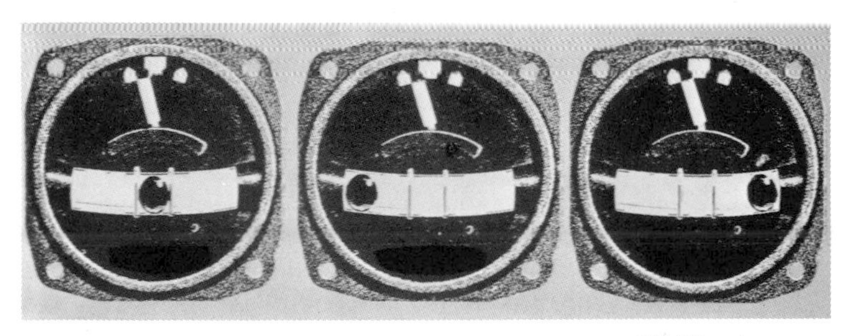

7.7 The turn-and-slip indicator
COURTESY OF FEDERAL AVIATION AGENCY

controls to suit. The autopilot can keep the airplane on a heading, keep it at a certain altitude, and keep the wings level. It can do these things more accurately than the human pilot, and can take over the flying so that the pilot can perform other duties.

To many people, the most amazing equipment on the instrument panel is the radio gear. At almost any time, almost any place in the United States, you can press the button of your radio microphone and talk instantly with an FAA radio facility on the ground. The electronic ground equipment of FAA is equally astonishing. Almost anywhere in the United States, if you are flying on an airway at a reasonably high altitude, your airplane will be visible as a speck of light on one of the FAA's radarscopes. The sky may seem empty and lonely, but radio signals are everywhere, zipping between airplane and airplane, between airplane and ground. Some of the signals from the ground are broadcast to tell the pilot where he is. With proper equipment, he can find his way through the trackless sky entirely by radio aids.

The magic that the little black box full of tubes, transistors, and wires can produce is made possible by the fact that energy can be transmitted as electromagnetic waves. Other types of energy travel in waves, too. We are familiar with the surface waves that move outward in a circular pattern when a stone is tossed into a pond. Sound is brought to our ears by pressure waves that travel through the air.

Radio waves are little bundles of energy that are part of the *electromagnetic spectrum,* which also includes light and heat energy. Visible light, because we can see it, is the part of the spectrum with which we are most familiar. All electromagnetic waves are alike in that they travel at the speed of light, 186,000 miles per second, and can travel through the vacuum of space, but they have other characteristics that are very different for different frequencies.

Visible light, for example, is transmitted in a very tiny wave that vibrates around a million billion times per second and measures only 1/25,000 to 1/50,000 of a centimeter in wavelength. (Wavelength is measured as the distance between two consecutive waves, as between two adjacent ripples in a pond wave.) Electromagnetic waves that vibrate more slowly and have a longer wavelength are called *infrared,* or heat waves, while the still longer wave lengths, from 1 centimeter to more than 1,000,000 centimeters, are called *radio waves.*

Developed only a few years before the airplane, radio was still very new in the early days of aviation. Radio communication between two airplanes was first demonstrated in 1916. Early radio equipment had many disadvantages and problems. Because it was heavy and used a great deal of power, it was not often carried on small airplanes. The low frequencies used had the same static problems that make your AM radio noisy or perhaps unusable during a thunderstorm. Also, these low frequencies (long wavelengths) required very long antennas for both sending and receiving. For an antenna some airplanes used a long trailing wire that was dragged behind in flight and reeled in before landing.

But after World War II, the new wartime technology made possible a new and very different kind of radio. Using frequencies in the Very High Frequency (VHF) range (30 to 300 megacycles), the new equipment is lighter in weight and requires only a small "whip" antenna half the size of an automobile antenna. Most important of all, VHF radio is static-free, and can even transmit right through a thunderstorm. VHF radio has one disadvantage compared to low-frequency radio. Low-frequency radio waves can travel for long distances beyond the horizon because they follow the surface of the earth (or in some cases are reflected back to earth from the top layers of the atmosphere). VHF radio waves, on the other hand, travel in straight lines, like light. Only stations that are in "line of sight" of each other are able to communicate. For communication between stations on the ground, VHF would have very short range because the curvature of the earth soon puts two stations out of sight of each other. But in the air at even a moderate altitude, an airplane will still be "in line of sight" with a ground station fifty or more miles away and able to talk with the station.

Just as an electric lamp sends out light that can be seen by our eyes, the radio transmitter emits radio energy that can be "seen," or received, by special equipment. The details of how the message is carried by radio waves is beyond the scope of this chapter — for our purposes here we can say that the message to be sent is "impressed" on the waves, changing their amplitude (wave height) or frequency (distance between waves). At the receiving end, the message is read or taken off the waves in the reverse process.

The use of radio by aircraft has grown rapidly, and most of the private aircraft in this country carry at least one radio. Obviously, not everyone can talk on the radio at one time, like on a telephone party line. The VHF range for aircraft communications has been divided up into 360 frequencies or "channels" for voice communication and another 100 channels for navigation facilities. The frequencies used by control towers, flight service stations, air traffic control, and other

FAA facilities, are assigned throughout the country in a way that will help to prevent interference. But many frequencies are so busy that you may have to listen for awhile and wait for a lull in the traffic to get your message in.

The best radio equipment would be useless if there was no one listening for your call. Fortunately, there are many people listening, ready to give information or other help to the pilot, nearly everywhere in the United States. In 1969, some 336 Flight Service Stations dotted the country from coast to coast. Press the microphone button and you can talk to a specialist who can tell you about the weather anywhere in the country, handle your flight plan request or cancellation, or give you almost any other help you might need.

It you are flying on an instrument flight plan, you will talk regularly with the *Air Traffic Control Center* controlling your area. These centers, such as the Houston Center, Cleveland Center, New York Center, and so on, use radar equipment and radio communications to follow and control all instrument (IFR) traffic on the airways.

Radar, which obtained its name from the phrase RAdio Detection And Ranging, developed into an extremely important device during World War II. Radar is based upon the reflection of electromagnetic waves. The radar station on the ground sweeps a radio signal through the sky in all directions. When the signal strikes an airplane, it bounces off and is reflected back to the station. There it appears as a spot of light or "blip" on the operator's electronic screen. From this blip the operator can tell the direction and distance of the "target" from the station. Because it depends upon a weak reflected signal, the effectiveness of radar is limited by distance and the size of the target. Also, the operator cannot easily tell one blip from another because they all look alike.

Most large airplanes and many small ones have a special black box called a *transponder* that helps the radar on the ground to find and identify each airplane. When the transponder receives the radar signal from the ground, it answers with a signal of its own that is much stronger than the reflected signal. In addition, the stronger signal can be coded so that the radar operator can tell just which blip on his screen is which airplane.

At many busy points in the country you can talk with *approach control* which will guide you along proper paths through the area or to a landing at any airport in that area. Most approach-control facilities have radar equipment with which they can observe your exact position and warn you of other traffic in your vicinity. In bad weather they can guide you (or as they say *vector* you) to the "instrument approach" where your own equipment takes over to guide you down through the clouds to a landing. With some radar equipment the controller can "talk the pilot down" to the runway by watching his path on a scope and telling him which way to steer and how fast to descend.

At more than three hundred busy airports in the United States, your radio will be used to contact the FAA *control tower* for landing and takeoff instructions. At such airports it would be impossible for each pilot to plan his own landing and fit in with other traffic without guidance from the ground. You must have a two-way radio to land at most of these airports. Approach control may vector incoming airplanes toward the airport, give them proper spacing, and turn them over to the control tower. The tower then assigns the proper runway, and continues to space the traffic so that each aircraft has enough time to complete his landing and taxi off the runway before the next airplane touches down. As you take off from such an airport, a separate *departure control* may vector you away from incoming traffic and guide you out of the control zone to the airway you desire.

The equipment on the panel of a modern airplane has played a vital part in making the airplane a safe, useful, and fast means of transportation. The pilot of the modern light-plane must know more than just how to fly the airplane through certain maneuvers; he must have a broad understanding of the airplane and all of its equipment. He must also have a detailed knowledge of the vast communications, navigation, and air traffic systems spread throughout the country. These systems are instantly available to the pilot at the press of his microphone button — if he knows how to use it.

8

Learning to Fly

AFTER MY FIRST SOLO FLIGHT many years ago, my instructor delivered a little lecture. I should not, he said, waste time just flying around aimlessly looking at the scenery. Instead, I should keep working hard on the maneuvers and skills necessary to pass the flight test for a private license.

It was good advice. But the first time I was permitted to leave the airport traffic pattern, I wasted a whole hour just flying around looking at the scenery. I couldn't help it. Learning to fly had been hard work. For eight or ten hours I had concentrated so hard on doing the maneuvers I was asked to do that I had lost the feel and purpose of flying. I remember being startled to find, after one long session of dual airwork, that I didn't know where we were. I had paid so little attention to the ground while working on maneuvers that I had unwittingly drifted nearly twenty miles from our starting point in the practice area.

So for that whole hour after solo I flew around, relaxed,

and enjoyed myself. I explored the countryside and towns below, an area I had lived in for many years, like a tourist seeing the sights for the first time. I climbed up to the base of the scattered clouds because I could, and after triumphantly viewing the world from there, throttled back the noisy engine for a long, quiet glide back down again. Just me, the airplane and the world — oh, yes, and that empty seat behind me. This flight sticks in my memory as vividly as the first solo. On the first solo I proved that I could be there alone; on this flight I rediscovered my desire and purpose for being there. On my next flight I was ready to go back to work.

Learning to fly is fun. Whether or not the fledgling pilot finds it easy, it is an exacting art that demands effort and attention. If he takes his flying seriously (and he *should*) he will likely find it hard work at first, with the fun increasing as time goes on. Flying is different: it's a challenge, a whole new world of motion and sensation, a new point of view.

The pilot must develop new and expanded skills. Instead of steering only left or right as we do on the ground, he now has the added dimension of up and down. He also must be prepared to be in constant motion. There is no traffic light at which he can pause to think about his next turn, no roadside shoulder where he can stop to read his roadmap. He will be traveling at high speed from the beginning to the end of his flight, and must always be planning ahead to his next maneuver, and to the next. If he misjudges his approach to a landing field or finds traffic in his way, he cannot stop and think about his situation — he must keep moving and maneuver safely and smoothly according to established procedures back into position for another approach.

Although there is less traffic in the sky than on the ground, the pilot must be constantly watching for traffic from all directions. On the highway, signs may warn of an approaching intersection and cars do not jump out of the bushes to cross our path. But in the air, an intersection may exist anywhere — wherever the paths of two airplanes happen to cross, and an airplane may jump out from behind any cloud.

The pilot must develop a new caution and a new respect for the machine upon which his very life depends while he is aloft. Many people leap into their cars and roar away without having looked even to see whether all four wheels are still attached. The service-station attendant may check "under the hood" when a car is fueled, but he may fail to do so unless we ask. Instead of giving their automobiles regular service, many people simply get them fixed when something stops working.

The pilot can take no such chances. It is too important to him that the airplane operate properly and *keep* operating while he is in the air. So the pilot runs a preflight inspection *every time he flies.* Not just a quick look to see if all the pieces are hanging together, but a thorough inspection to prove that the airplane is ready and able to fly (figure 8.1). The inspection procedure varies somewhat with the type of aircraft, but contains the same elements. Are all aerodynamic surfaces in good condition? All control surfaces operating, all hinges okay? Sometimes an airplane can be damaged while it is being moved in the hangar. Even a small bend in a control surface can be dangerous. Are all control cables fastened securely?

Flap and flap hinges. Landing gear. Tire pressures. Engine oil level. Engine cooling-air passages — any bird nests? They've been found there. Pitot-static head. The propeller — any nicks, scratches, cracks? Engine cowling and propeller spin-

8.1 Author giving his plane a preflight inspection
COURTESY OF VIRGINIA DEFOY

ner — securely fastened? Fuel tanks. The pilot should check fuel quantity himself, and be sure that tank caps are on tight and that the vents are open. A small amount of gas should be drained from the cock below each tank and at the fuel pump to check for water or sediment and to regularly remove the tiny amounts of these that may accumulate in the bottoms of the tanks.

And so it goes. The pilot should develop a regular step-by-step procedure for the preflight checkout and follow it carefully. It's a serious business. One morning on a small island in the Caribbean my preflight check turned up over a cup of water and sediment in the bottom of each fuel tank. Several hot days and humid, cool nights had condensed that much water in the half-empty fuel tanks. If this water had not been removed, chances are good that the engine would have started and checked out satisfactorily, but would have quit on takeoff when the water reached the engine. There would have been no place to land except in the ocean.

A thorough cockpit check is also vital. Engine gauges. Fuel tank selector. Engine controls. All instruments operating and set. Trim set. Controls free and surfaces moving in proper direction. Surprising as it may seem, controls have been connected in reverse after adjustment or overhaul, and serious accidents almost always result if the pilot takes off with his controls working backwards! Seat belt fastened. Doors latched.

A check of the engine in the "run-up" is the final item. Just before takeoff, with the brakes set (and the airplane pointed so that it won't blow dust on anyone) the engine is run up to the speed specified for that engine (often about two-thirds of takeoff RPM). The ignition switch is turned to operate the engine on first one ignition system (magneto), then the other, then both at once. If improper operation on either magneto is found, the cause should be eliminated before the airplane is flown.

Words in a book cannot teach anyone to fly, or even give a very useful account of what happens to the fellow in the student's seat. The whole process varies greatly depending upon both the student and the instructor. This chapter will instead describe in a general way the basic maneuvers, how they are made, and what some of the problems are.

For all its complication, flying boils down to only a few simple maneuvers. The three basic ones are the *climb,* the *descent* (or glide), and the *turn.* The *stall* is a fourth, although it is not really a normal flight maneuver but one that is used (or closely approached) only at the instant of landing. Then there is that important nonmaneuver, *straight-and-level flight,* which might be called the absence of all the basic maneuvers. All ordinary flight is made up of the above maneuvers or combinations of them.

For the first few flying lessons, the instructor will usually make the takeoffs and landings, using them as demonstrations, with the student "following through" on the controls to learn how the controls are moved. The classroom for these first few hours is mostly high in the air, where the student can practice one maneuver at a time, after demonstration by the instructor. Then he can begin to put the maneuvers together that will be required for takeoff and landing operations.

At the practice altitude, the airplane must first be "trimmed" for level flight. Engine power (RPM) is set and the elevator trim tab adjusted so that the airplane will fly level "hands-off." This is the level-flight condition, the beginning and end of all maneuvers, the attitude in which airplanes (except perhaps trainers) spend most of their time. The pilot must look carefully at the position of the airplane nose ahead of him and the position of the wing tips to his right and left with respect to the horizon. He must learn to return the airplane to these positions by eye in order to maintain level flight, using the airplane's instruments as a check and for final small adjustments (figure 8.2).

Straight-and-level flight

Climb

Climbing turn

Level turn

Glide

Gliding turn

8.2 The view from the cockpit during the basic maneuvers. Note readings of instruments. COURTESY OF DOUGLAS W. SMITH

Although straight-and-level flight sounds easy, the student pilot may find it hard work until he begins to get the hang of it. You finally get the wings level at the assigned altitude and compass course, and say to yourself: "Now I have it!" A moment later the altimeter tells you that you are climbing a little. You move the elevator control to correct this, and a slight bank begins to turn the airplane off course. You arrive at your altitude again and bank the airplane slightly the other way, only to find as you arrive back on course that you are diving just a little. You move the elevator to correct that . . . and so it goes. You wallow across the sky trying to get everything nailed down at once. Of course you never quite succeed, because flying requires constant attention and continual operation of controls. But you begin to see unwanted turns and climbs and glides earlier and to make automatic corrections while they are very small. You also learn that the stability of a good airplane will help a great deal, particularly in rough air. If a bump rocks the airplane, wait a moment. The airplane will probably correct most of the way back by itself. Letting it do so means less work for the pilot and a smoother, more gentle ride for the passengers.

Before you master the straight-and-level maneuver, your instructor will start you on turns. With the ailerons you roll the airplane into a bank so that the wing can turn the airplane. If you use *only* the ailerons, the airplane will "yaw" (or turn its nose) the other way — that is, to the right while you are rolling to the left. This wrong-way turn, which is known as "adverse yaw," is caused partly by the fact that the down-deflected aileron may have more drag than the up-deflected aileron. A more important cause is the fact that the lift force on the down-going wing tilts a bit forward while the lift on the up-going wing tilts a bit rearward. Both of the effects combine to produce a sloppy skidding action as you roll into or out of a turn unless a little rudder is used *while the airplane is rolling* — just enough to keep the ball of the slip indicator in the center. Left aileron, left rudder; right aileron, right rudder — a little practice with one eye on the ball and you will soon find the right amount of rudder for a particular airplane.

On most airplanes a little back pressure on the elevator will be needed in a turn to increase the angle of attack of the wing. The wing will then generate the extra lift needed to turn the airplane while also supporting it in level flight. The steeper the bank, the more extra lift will be needed.

Around you go in a level turn, trying to keep the angle of bank constant, and the altitude constant, rolling out again at the proper point. You will probably use highways or other landmarks for making a quarter turn (90°), a half turn (180°), or a full turn (360°). After using opposite aileron *and rudder* to roll back to straight and level for a few moments, you will probably hear the instructor call for a turn in the opposite direction. Watch that bank angle . . . altitude . . . bank angle . . . altitude . . . and so it goes.

Climbs and glides are next — and here we run into one of the many cases in flight where things don't happen as you might expect. The idea most people have of the elevator control is that we pull back on the wheel (or stick) to go *up* and push forward to go *down.* Also that we advance the throttle to speed up and retard the throttle to slow down. Both ideas are quite inaccurate and quite dangerous to a pilot. The truth is that the function of the throttle and elevator are quite the opposite of the common idea — the throttle is really the *altitude* control and the elevator the *speed* control.

It is easy to accept the throttle as an altitude control. If we want to climb, we must add more power to pull the plane "uphill." When we descend, we must reduce power to keep speed from increasing too much as the airplane moves "downhill." But it is more difficult to accept the elevator as a *speed* control. In Chapter 3 we learned that the elevator changes the balance of the airplane — increases or decreases its *angle of attack.* At a high angle of attack (control wheel back) the airplane will fly slowly, and at a low angle of attack (wheel forward) the airplane will fly at a higher speed. To produce enough lift to fly, you will remember, the airplane can either give a small amount of air a large deflection (low speed, large angle of attack) or give a large amount of air a small deflection (high speed, small angle of attack).

So to enter a climb, you must advance the throttle to make the engine produce more power for climbing, and pull back on the elevator control to point the nose upward and to obtain climb speed. A little back movement on the wheel will give you a fast speed and a small climb angle that will gain altitude slowly; a larger movement will pull the nose up for a slower speed and a steeper climb. If you pull back too far, you could reach a stall, which we'll cover a little later.

To enter a glide, you reduce power and move the elevator control to obtain the glide speed you want. In most airplanes, you will pull the wheel back a little to obtain a moderate glide speed, or a little more for a slower glide speed. It's quieter now with the engine idling, and you can hear the air swooshing past the airplane. As you glide, you must hold your wings level, airspeed constant. Hold that heading, you're turning to the left, airspeed too high, you're turning to the right — as always, you must watch all of the airplane's attitudes at once!

In making glides at various speeds, you soon learn that there is a certain speed at which the airplane will glide the greatest distance. At slower speeds, the airplane will lose altitude more rapidly. Drag due to lift is "putting on the brakes." This drag, you will recall from Chapter 3, increases as angle of attack increases. Hence, the slower you go, the larger your angle of attack must be, and the more steeply you will descend. Glide speed is thus your most important tool in controlling the landing approach. Here you have another case in flying where things do not happen as you might think. If we are a bit too low on the approach, we must keep the nose *down* so that the speed will remain higher and the airplane will glide the maximum distance. (A little power from the engine might also be needed.) If we are a bit too high, we must *raise* the nose (pull back on the wheel) to slow the airplane so that it will descend more steeply. This is why the pilot should *always* regard the elevator as a *speed* control rather than an *altitude* control. The pilot must resist the temptation to pull back on the elevator control to try to stretch his glide and keep the airplane in the air. Doing so would only increase the steepness of his descent and perhaps put him into the bushes just short of the runway.

Every airplane has its own particular speeds for lift-off, climb, landing approach, and touchdown. The pilot must know the recommended speed and power settings for his airplane for all flight conditions if he is to fly the airplane safely and well.

And now, as though things are not complicated enough, you

will be asked to combine a climb and a turn, and a glide and a turn. This is really not much more difficult — instead of keeping your wings level in a climb or glide, you simply keep them at a constant angle of bank. Now you must watch air-speed, bank angle, heading, and roll out when you should. Things are getting busier all the time! Now turn in the other direction. Airspeed, bank angle, direction, airspeed, bank angle . . .

After a few hours of hard work, you will begin to feel that you are getting the hang of it. And you have learned almost enough to put the basic maneuvers together in the landing and takeoff operations.

Two more maneuvers are needed before we can start landings and takeoffs: the *stall,* and flight at very slow speeds — known simply as *slow flight.*

The purpose of slow flight is to acquaint the student with the feel of the airplane at speeds all the way down to stalling speed. When he knows how the airplane and its controls feel and respond at speeds approaching the stall, he is not so likely to get into this dangerous speed range unintentionally. He must, of course, fly the airplane at slow speeds during a landing approach, and must slow to a stall, or nearly to a stall, when he is about to touch down on the runway.

The place to practice this kind of flying is high in the air, not next to the ground. So we climb to a safe altitude of several thousand feet over open country and throttle back the engine a little. With a little back pressure on the wheel you hold the nose up to increase the angle of attack and keep the airplane in level flight, neither losing nor gaining altitude. Your speed is now well below cruising speed. Now you try a level turn, and find the airplane sluggish and slow to respond.

But it still flies. Throttling the engine back still more, you find that more back pressure is needed on the elevator control to hold the airplane in level flight. With less and less speed, the airplane needs more and more angle of attack. The nose is now uncomfortably high in front of you. In a turn the airplane is even more sluggish and mushy. A little slower and the airplane will begin to tremble and rumble a bit, which tells you that the wing is beginning to stall. Over the area of the wing near the fuselage, the air is not following the upper surface of the airfoil, but is tearing away and swirling back in a rough, wild pattern. When you try to make a turn at this speed, more of the wing may stall and the airplane may suddenly drop. Some airplanes will give the pilot a nasty surprise in a stall from slow flight — rolling sharply off into a spiral or even a spin. Most of today's lightplanes are more docile than that, but the place to learn about such surprises, if the airplane has any to show, is up at a safe altitude.

Now you are ready for a full stall. In level cruising flight, throttle the engine all the way back to idle, and slowly move the wheel back to hold the nose up a little higher than for level flight. The airspeed will drop rapidly and the airplane feels heavier and more "mushy." It may begin to rumble and shake as the wing begins to stall or as the rough flow from the wing begins to strike the horizontal tail. The angle of attack of the wing finally becomes so large, about the time you get the wheel all the way back, that the air can no longer follow the top surface of a large portion of the wing smoothly, but tears away from it and swirls back in a useless churning action. The wing then loses a significant amount of lift and the airplane begins to fall (figure 8.3). What happens next depends upon what kind of an airplane you're flying. Most light airplanes

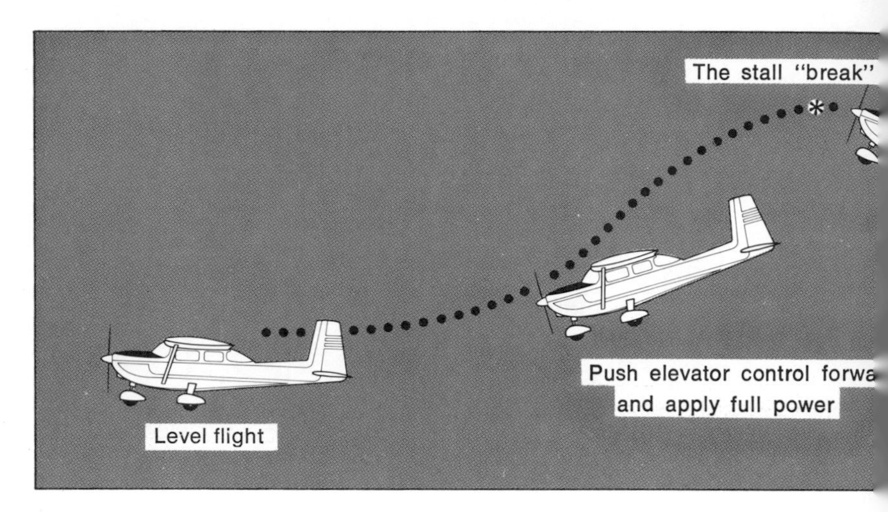

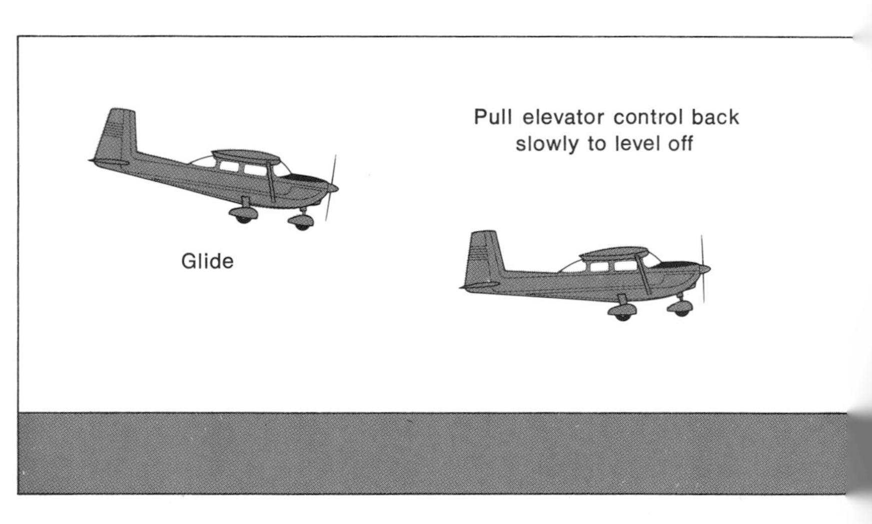

8.5 The landing

Pull wheel back slowly
Level flight

8.3 The stall

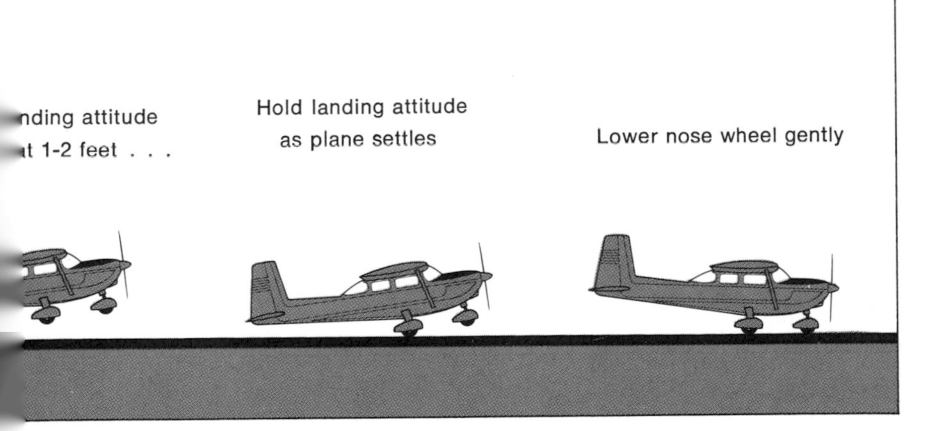
nding attitude
t 1-2 feet . . .
Hold landing attitude
as plane settles
Lower nose wheel gently

are designed to stall gently. Because of a twist designed into the wing, the tips are at a lower angle of attack than the center of the wing. Consequently, the center section near the fuselage stalls first, leaving the tips unstalled and the ailerons near the tip still able to control the airplane in roll. Because only a part of the wing is stalled, even with the elevator control all the way back, most light airplanes shake and rumble in a stall, and the nose drops slightly and nothing important seems to happen. But if you look at the altimeter, you will find that you are losing altitude fast! And herein lies the great danger of the stall. The stalled airplane is not flying smoothly but just mushing through the air and sinking rapidly toward the ground.

To get it flying again, the wing must be "unstalled." The pilot must push the elevator control *forward* (nose down) to decrease angle of attack, at the same time increasing engine power, to get the airplane up to flying speed again. It may seem strange to push the nose *down* when the airplane is already sinking toward the ground at an alarming rate, but there is no other way to decrease the angle of attack and establish flying speed again. This is perhaps the most important condition to which a student pilot must learn to react quickly and correctly. When near a stall, or when actually mushing downward in a stall, the natural reaction might be to pull back on the wheel to stop the airplane from sinking toward the ground. But this natural reaction would only make matters worse. The pilot must first dive a little to regain flying speed and *then* stop the airplane's descent by returning to level flight. The heavier the airplane, the more altitude will be lost in regaining flying speed. This is why a stall at low altitude is so dangerous. The pilot may not have enough altitude to get his airplane flying again before he runs into the ground.

You will practice stalls from glides and from gliding turns to show you how they feel and to give you practice in recovering from an unintentional stall in a landing approach. Stalls in climbs and climbing turns will show you how the airplane might behave if stalled while you were climbing out of an airport after takeoff. In all cases you must act quickly and correctly to get the airplane flying again and under control with minimum loss of altitude.

Having practiced all of the basic maneuvers and tested the airplane's character in slow flight and in stalls, you are ready for landings and takeoffs. All airplanes must use the same approach and departure "pattern" around an airport. If they did not, traffic would be shooting in and out from all directions and at all altitudes, and no one would know where to look for other airplanes or whose turn it was to land. So most airports use the same general traffic pattern, with variations to suit local conditions. A typical traffic pattern for a noncontrolled field is shown in figure 8.4.

Takeoffs and landings are always made as close as possible *into the wind* in order to make ground speed as small as possible. For example, assume that the wind is blowing 15 miles per hour and lift-off speed for your airplane is 65 miles per hour. Because the air is moving 15 miles per hour over the airplane before it starts to move, the airplane needs to accelerate to a ground speed of only 50 miles per hour ($65 - 15 = 50$) to take off if it is headed into the wind. But if we took off downwind, our ground speed would need to be $65 + 15$, or 80 miles per hour. Obviously, an airplane needs less runway to land or take off into the wind. Even the birds know this — watch a bird land in a tree or on the ground

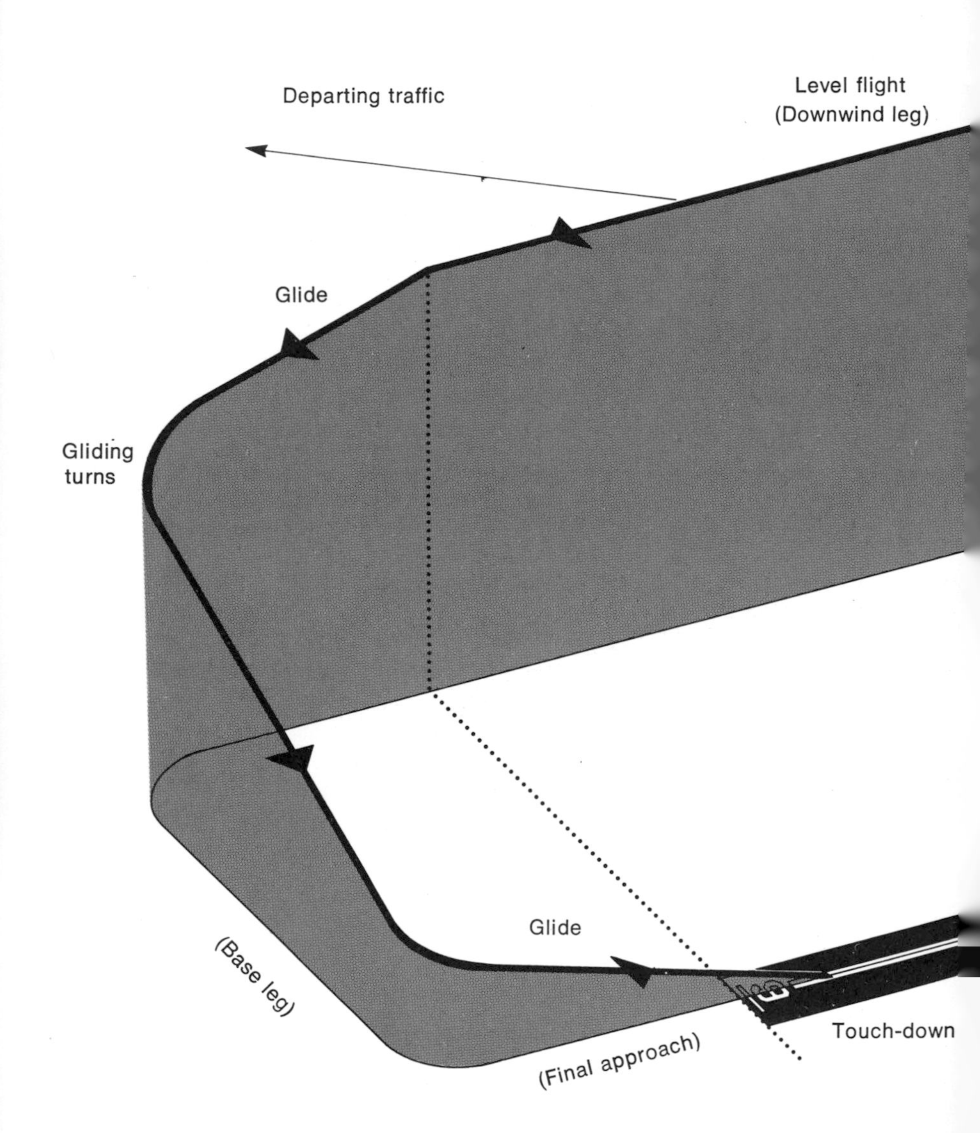
Departing traffic
Level flight
(Downwind leg)
Glide
Gliding turns
Glide
(Base leg)
(Final approach)
Touch-down

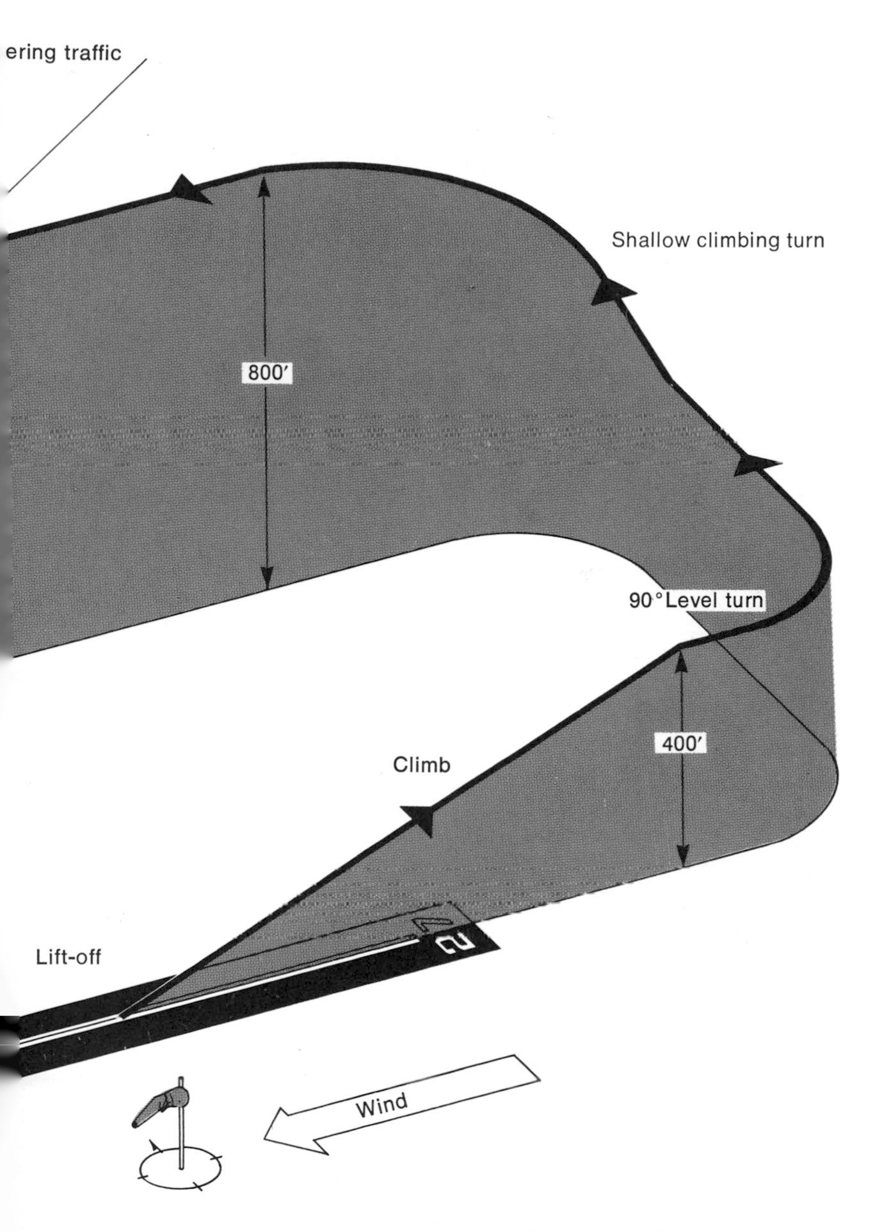

8.4 A typical airport traffic pattern

when the wind is blowing and you will see that he always lands into the wind so that he can touch down at a very small forward speed.

In approaching the airport, you must check the *wind sock* or *wind tee* to find the direction of the wind. You then visualize the landing pattern as attached to the particular runway that will let you land into the wind.

Shall we take it around once now, and put all the maneuvers together? With the cockpit check and engine run-up complete, we check to see that there is no traffic coming in and taxi into position on the runway. (On a controlled field we would first obtain a takeoff clearance from the tower.) Opening the throttle smoothly, we accelerate down the runway, steering the airplane with the rudder pedals. As we reach flying speed, we ease back on the wheel to increase the angle of attack of the wing, and the airplane leaves the ground. With our speed adjusted to the proper climb speed with the elevator, we climb straight ahead to 400 feet and throttle back to level flight. After looking around to be sure there is no other traffic in our way, we bank to the left for a 90° level turn. Rolling out, we increase the throttle to climb power once again and bring the nose up to climb speed. After a shallow 90° climbing turn to the left (look around first) we continue to climb to 800 feet and level off, throttling back to cruise power once more. We are now flying downwind, parallel to the runway, and in a few moments will be in position for our landing approach. We glance over the landing checklist and complete all items. As we pass the end of the runway we apply carburetor heat (if required), close the throttle and bring the airplane to proper approach (glide) speed, gliding straight ahead. At the proper time, we make a 90° gliding turn to the left (look around first). We are now on "base leg" where we can make adjustments to our pattern. The end of the runway is ahead and to our left. If we're a little low we can aim a bit to the left toward the end of the runway. If we're a bit high we can aim a bit to the right to lengthen our glide in order to use up unwanted altitude before we get to the runway. A small deflection of the flaps here on base leg is common practice, if the airplane has flaps. We must start our turn in time to roll out on "final approach." Look around, start a 90° gliding turn to the left, roll out on final, aimed right down the runway. Too high? We'll apply a little back elevator (nose up) to slow our approach just a bit so that the airplane will glide more steeply, and add more flap as needed. Too low? We'll apply a little forward elevator (nose down) to glide faster and less steeply. A little power may be needed. Add more flaps when needed. We're over the runway threshold now, bring the wheel back slowly to level off. Keep the airplane flying just a foot or so over the runway, keep the wheel moving slowly back, keep it flying, wheel back . . . suddenly the airplane touches softly on the main wheels (figure 8.5). We lower the nose wheel gently by easing the elevator control forward and concentrate on holding the airplane straight along the runway with the rudder pedals until it has slowed enough to turn off onto the taxiway.

The whole flight takes only a few minutes, but it's a busy few minutes! This is the payoff, the exercise where the student proves that he can not only perform the maneuvers, but put them all together and fly the airplane along a required path. When the student shows that he can do this, after eight hours or more of dual instruction, the instructor begins to think about turning him loose for the big adventure — first solo. One day when the student is making good landings, and the traffic is not too heavy, the instructor will say as they taxi back for another takeoff:

"Stop here for a moment.

"Let me out! I can't stand it any longer!" he may quip as he climbs out. Or he may quietly give some words of advice or encouragement.

"Three times around, then bring it back to the hangar." Trying to act nonchalant, he may pretend not to be watching as he strolls back to the hangar. But he is. He alone is responsible for the decision to send the student up by himself. Actually, the hazard of the first solo is negligible if the student is well trained and ready, and many pilots will claim that their own flying that day could hardly have been better.

After the student has lost his shirttail on that memorable day, he really begins to learn about flying. When he is up there alone, he has only himself to rely upon, and he must criticize and correct his own performance. On his next few lessons, the instructor will ride around in the pattern a few times and then get out again, for a second and third "supervised solo." By this time the student has proved his ability to the point where the instructor may let him leave the pattern to fly locally and to a practice area, without further supervision or permission. The instructor will ride with him occasionally to check his progress, to work with him on the maneuvers he must perform for the flight test, and to help him correct his mistakes.

During his minimum of forty hours of flight training, he will be flying solo more than half the time. Ten hours will be spent on cross-country flights, one trip with the instructor aboard, the others solo, to give the student experience in planning and navigating such flights.

The license test, like the solo flight, is another important milestone, but not the end of learning. When the student has shown the examiner that he understands the basics of flight, can apply them, can navigate and operate the airplane in a safe fashion, he will be awarded his private license. Now he can carry passengers (not for hire) and can use an airplane for business and pleasure travel. He can work toward advanced licenses: instrument rating, commercial license, air transport rating, or even a seaplane or helicopter rating. But whatever his goals, he will continue to learn about flying as long as he flies.

9

Navigation

SUPPOSE THAT YOU WERE to take off from your city to fly to another town a hundred miles away. How would you find your way? If you knew the countryside well enough, you might follow a river, or a railroad, or even a highway that goes there. You would hope that you would be able to recognize your destination from the air and not get lost on the way. This is just how cross-country flying was done in the very early days of aviation. Railroad tracks were used so much by pilots that they were called "the iron compass." But too often no river or railroad goes where you want to go. Highways are not easy to follow from the air, and they all look so much alike that one can easily get confused. Then, too, one of the big advantages of air travel is to be able to move in a straight line over all obstacles, rather than following some crooked path on the ground.

In order to do a good job today of flying from one place to another, we need good maps, or charts, and a knowledge of *navigation,* which may be defined simply as the art or science of directing the airplane where you want to go. Surprisingly enough, navigation is not at all difficult, and with the development of radio aids, has become amazingly easy.

There are three basic methods used in aircraft navigation today: *dead reckoning, pilotage,* and *radio navigation.* The first two are closely connected, and one, two, or all three methods may be used on the same flight.

A first requirement for finding our way around in the air is good *maps* of the ground. Many years ago automobile road maps were the only maps available. Charles A. Lindbergh tells in *The Spirit of St. Louis* of buying road maps in a drugstore and using them for navigating from San Diego to St. Louis. Highways were more useful as landmarks in 1927, of course, because there were fewer of them. Today road maps simply won't do. They are designed for automobile use, and only roads and towns and major rivers are shown. But which road is which? Which town is which? When you can't read road signs, the problem of telling one place from another becomes difficult. So a different kind of map is needed — one that shows features that can be recognized *from the air.* The U.S. Coast and Geodetic Survey puts out many kinds of maps, more accurately called *charts,* for aerial navigation. A sample of a *sectional chart,* the kind most used by private-airplane pilots, is shown in figure 9.1. These charts show cities and towns, major highways, railroads, airports, television towers, power lines, lakes, rivers, dams, mountains, and many other features, all drawn and located accurately so that their peculiar shapes or arrangements may be recognized from the air. Even racetracks, open-air theaters, oil fields, and open-pit mines are shown where such things might help a pilot to

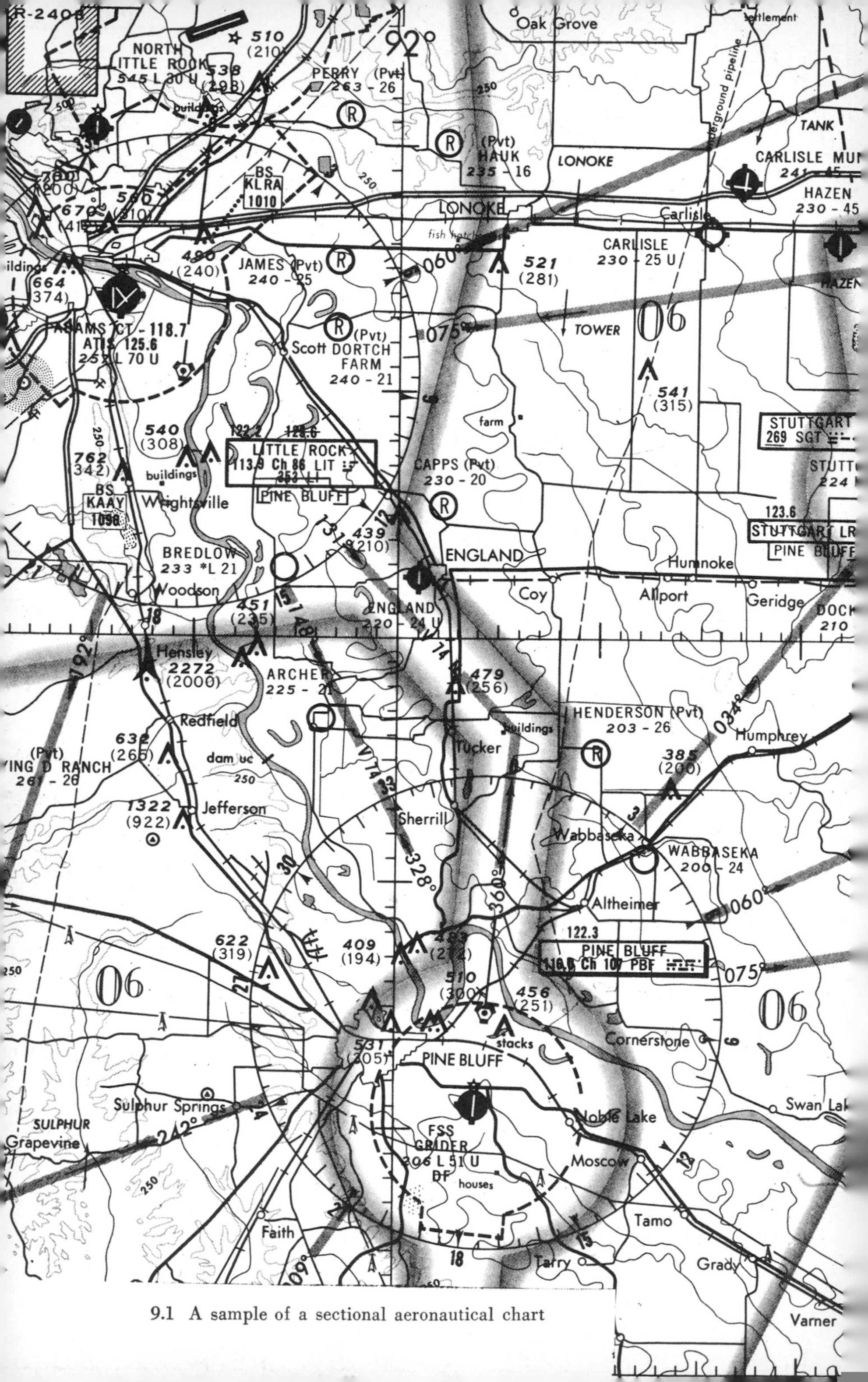

9.1 A sample of a sectional aeronautical chart

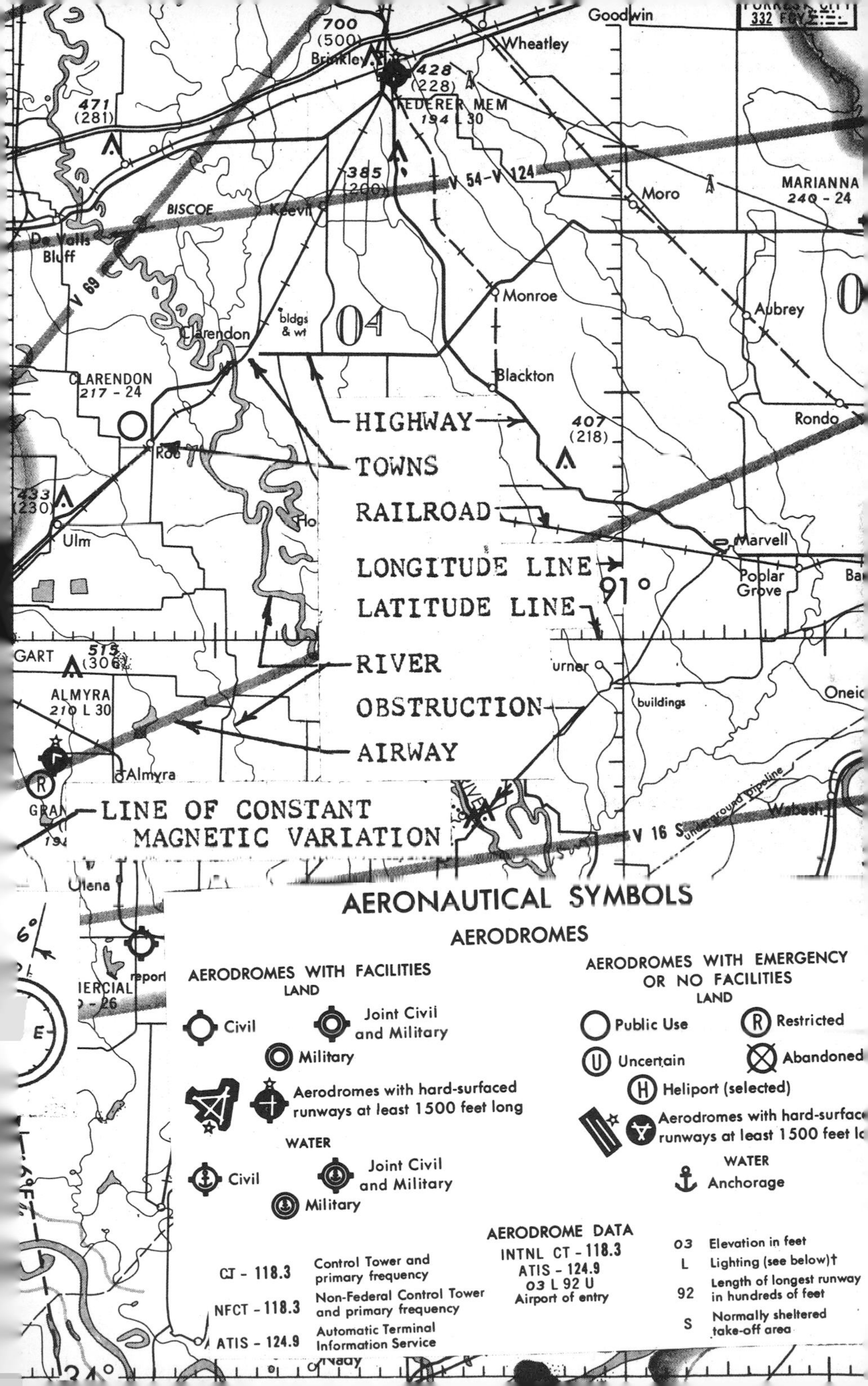
HIGHWAY
TOWNS
RAILROAD
LONGITUDE LINE
LATITUDE LINE
RIVER
OBSTRUCTION
AIRWAY
LINE OF CONSTANT MAGNETIC VARIATION
Goodwin
Wheatley
Brinkley
FEDERER MEM
194 L 30
V 54-V 124
Moro
MARIANNA
240 - 24
BISCOE
Keevil
De Valls Bluff
V 69
Monroe
Aubrey
bldgs & wt
Clarendon
CLARENDON
217 - 24
Blackton
Rondo
Roe
Ulm
Marvell
Poplar Grove
91°
Turner
buildings
ALMYRA
210 L 30
Almyra
underground pipeline
Wabash
V 16 S
Ulena
AERONAUTICAL SYMBOLS
AERODROMES
AERODROMES WITH FACILITIES
LAND
Civil
Joint Civil and Military
Military
Aerodromes with hard-surfaced runways at least 1500 feet long
WATER
Civil
Joint Civil and Military
Military
AERODROMES WITH EMERGENCY OR NO FACILITIES
LAND
Public Use
Restricted
Uncertain
Abandoned
Heliport (selected)
Aerodromes with hard-surfac runways at least 1500 feet lo
WATER
Anchorage
AERODROME DATA
INTNL CT - 118.3
ATIS - 124.9
03 L 92 U
Airport of entry
CT - 118.3 Control Tower and primary frequency
NFCT - 118.3 Non-Federal Control Tower and primary frequency
ATIS - 124.9 Automatic Terminal Information Service
03 Elevation in feet
L Lighting (see below)†
92 Length of longest runway in hundreds of feet
S Normally sheltered take-off area

identify his position on the ground. Airways and radio-navigation facilites are also shown. The entire continental United States and southern Canada are shown on about three dozen sectional charts. Larger-scale charts showing larger areas in less detail are also available as World Aeronautical Charts.

Charts of the earth's surface give us a means of not only knowing where we are, but also of measuring *distance* and *direction* between one point and another. In order to use a chart for navigation, we must understand how it was made and how it relates to the navigational equipment we use in the airplane.

The basis for all maps is the axis upon which the earth rotates. One end of this imaginary axis is the north pole, the other the south pole. The spherical surface of the earth can then be divided up by drawing "great circles" through the north and south poles (figure 9.2). These meridian lines seem

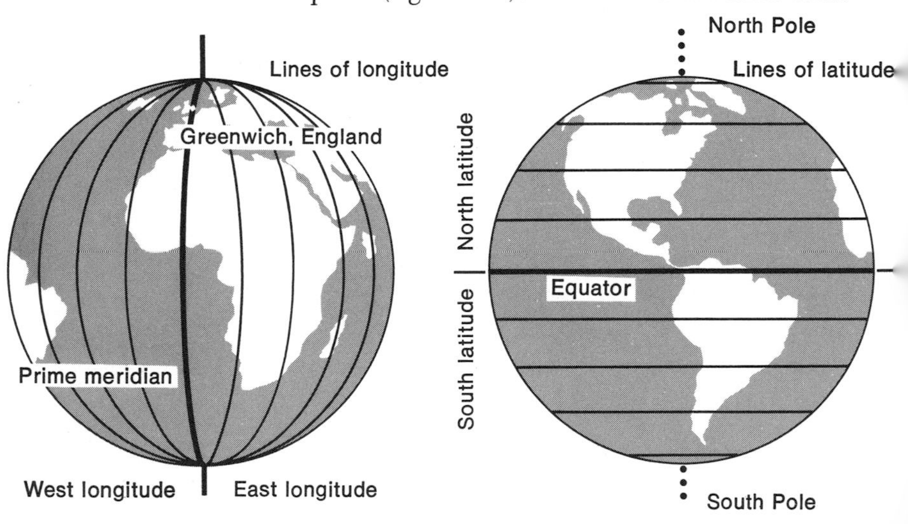

9.2 All aeronautical maps and charts are based on lines of longitude and latitude.

to cut the earth into sections, like an orange. The line that passes through Greenwich, England, is used as the starting point, with east and west longitude measured in degrees to the left and right of this *prime meridian.*

Another "great circle" is drawn around the earth halfway between the north and south poles. This is the *equator,* the starting point for north and south measurements. North and south latitude lines are circles drawn parallel to the equator that seem to cut the earth into slices, as shown in the sketch. Lines of latitude and longitude are shown on every map or chart, and give us "true" north and south and "true" east and west.

It would be convenient if the magnetic compass in the airplane pointed to true north, but it doesn't. It points instead to the earth's *magnetic* poles, which are located over a thousand miles from the geometric poles about which the earth rotates. For reasons that are not yet clearly understood, the magnetic poles move slowly over long periods of time. The error, or *variation,* between *true* north and *magnetic* north is therefore different for most places on the earth, and changes through the years. For use by pilots, surveyors, navigators, and others, the variation has been carefully measured and recorded on maps like the one in the illustration (figure 9.3). At any location on the dashed line marked "0°," the variation is zero and the magnetic compass will point true north, but at all other locations the compass will be in error by the amount indicated. For example, at New York City, the compass will point about 12° west of true north, an error large enough to cause trouble in navigation if not taken into account. Dashed lines showing the value of magnetic variation are shown on all aeronautical charts in order that the pilot may know at any point the relationship between his chart and his compass.

The other important thing the pilot needs to know about a chart is its *scale*. Sectional charts such as that shown in figure 9.1, for example, are drawn to a scale of eight miles to the inch. In planning a flight, we can now find the two points we wish to fly between and draw a line between them on the chart. If the distance on the chart is, say, $7\frac{1}{2}$ inches, the actual distance is $7\frac{1}{2} \times 8 = 60$ miles. Knowing the speed of our airplane, we can compute how long it will take to cover this distance. The *course* to our destination is designated by the compass heading and is measured in degrees from magnetic north. With a protractor we can measure the angle between

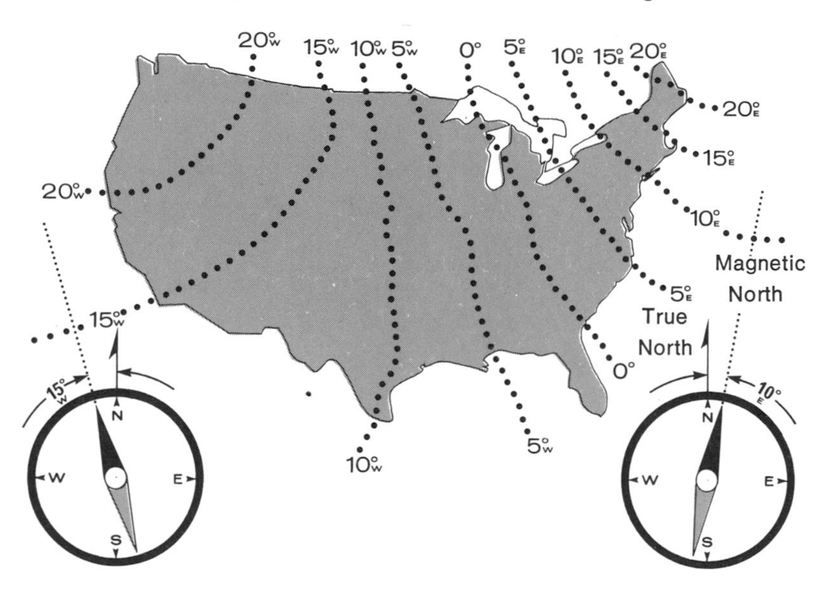

9.3 Isogonic chart shows lines of constant magnetic variation

our course on the chart and a "true north" line (any longitude line on the chart), add the variation angle for that location and perhaps a correction for our particular compass, if necessary, and obtain the compass course on which the airplane must travel.

But if we did all this, and carefully flew the measured course for the proper time, we might look on the ground below for our destination and not find it there. Why? The wind. While we were flying along on the course given by the chart, the air in which we were flying was itself moving in another direction. And so we drifted off course without knowing it, and missed our destination.

We tend to think of the wind as moving air that blows in our face. We can *feel* it that way, but that's just because we are standing still on the ground. The wind is really the motion of the whole body of air overhead. When the airplane is flying in this air, the wind does not "blow on it" but simply carries it along as it moves. On a still pond, a boat may move straight across in the direction in which its bow points. But on a swift river, a boat will be carried along downstream as it moves across and will not reach the point on the opposite bank toward which it seems headed. The wind carries an airplane with it in just this fashion.

The top diagram in figure 9.4 shows how the wind may drift an airplane off course. If we know our airspeed accurately and how fast the wind is blowing, we might plot a *new* course very precisely that would aim our airplane upwind (lower sketch) to allow for drift and would bring us closer to our destination. If we planned to fly over water or over a desert with few landmarks, we might have to rely upon such a carefully plotted course, using the clock to tell us when we're there. This method of navigating is called *dead reckoning*. If we find ourselves over our destination when we're supposed to be, we've done a good job, and the winds have been blowing as predicted. But if we missed, perhaps because the wind was not what it was supposed to be, we might have to look around for landmarks, find our position on the chart, and then set up a new course to our destination.

In most compass-and-chart navigation, pilots use a safer and simpler system known as *pilotage* — a combination of short dead-reckoning legs with checkpoints between. The pilot plots his compass course or estimates it as accurately as possible, then flies this heading, watching for his first "checkpoint." If his course calls for passing over a certain town, and the town appears to the left, he corrects his heading a bit to

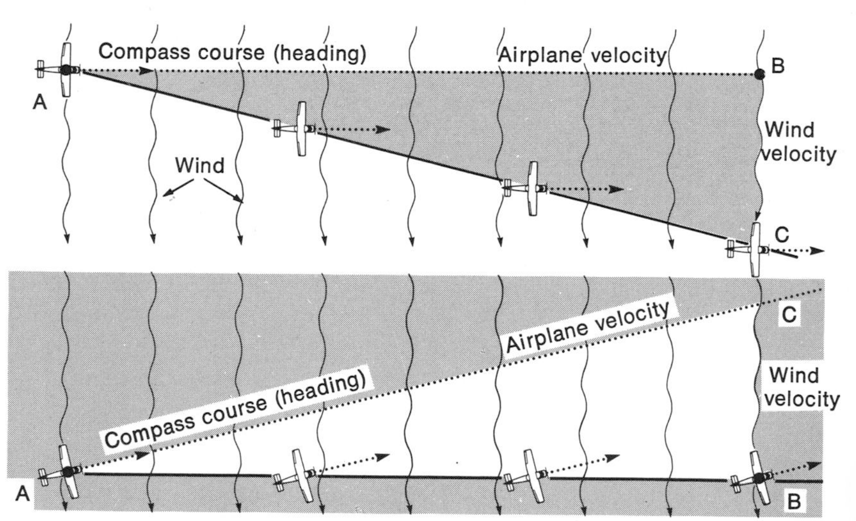

Airplane on compass course aimed at point B drifts with the wind and arrives at C, not B (top diagram)
With its compass course corrected for the wind, the airplane now aims at C, and drifts with the wind to arrive at B (bottom diagram)

9.4 Wind drift

the left. Then he flies his new heading carefully, watches for the next identifiable checkpoint, and corrects again if necessary. By measuring his time between checkpoints, he can determine his ground speed and the time when he will arrive. If his flight is a long one, he may use these in-flight calculations to decide where he will need to stop for fuel.

This system of navigation works very well when the pilot can see the ground and follow his progress on his chart. But how can a pilot find his way at night, when he cannot see towns, railroads, or rivers? Before the days of radio navigation, night flying was very difficult. Airway beacons were used in some parts of the country. Mounted on high hills or high towers, these rotating searchlights could be seen by a pilot for many miles on a clear night. Flying from one beacon to another, he simply followed the airway to his destination. But there were not very many lighted airways in the country — certainly not enough to fly anywhere a pilot might want to go. Many pilots, if they had to fly at night, used pilotage, with cities and a few other lighted landmarks as their checkpoints, and hoped that they could tell one city from another by its lights. When the weather was bad either in the daytime or at night, and the pilot could not see the ground, he could not fly — at least not safely.

The visible light transmitted by the airway beacon has the great advantage that we can *see* it with the human eye, and measure its direction from our position or travel toward it if we wish. But light has the great disadvantage that it does not travel through fog or clouds or rain. Unfortunately, clear, cloudless nights during which airplanes might navigate from one beacon to the next are rare.

Visible light, however, is only a small part of the whole

spectrum of electromagnetic energy that includes radio waves, heat, X rays, and others. Radio waves have the ability to pass readily through fog, clouds, and rain. With special equipment we can "see" these radio waves, measure the direction of the source, and travel toward it if we wish. The *radio compass* does just that. In the first airplane demonstration of the radio compass in 1920, an airplane flew out to sea to meet a Navy vessel and then flew back again to its land base, guided over the trackless ocean only by radio beacons on the ship and on shore.

The radio compass operates on the simple principle that a loop or flat coil of wire used as a receiving antenna will receive a station best when the loop is pointed edgewise toward it, and will pick up a station poorly, or not at all, when the loop is turned with its flat face toward the station.

The loop antennas for early radio compasses looked like large rings and were often mounted on the top or bottom of the rear fuselage. If the loop were fixed, the pilot would have to aim the whole airplane at a station in order to find his direction from it. Loops were therefore made rotatable so that the pilot could turn the loop to measure his bearing to a station without changing his flight course. The modern radio compass is completely automatic, and is called an *automatic direction finder*, or ADF. When tuned to a station, the ADF finds the direction to the station and shows it to the pilot on a panel indicator, measured from the axis of his airplane, in degrees (figure 9.5). The pilot can take a bearing from several stations, plot them on his chart, and determine exactly where he is. Or he can "fly the needle" from one station to the next without needing to look at the ground. The FAA and many states and cities maintain over five hundred radio bea-

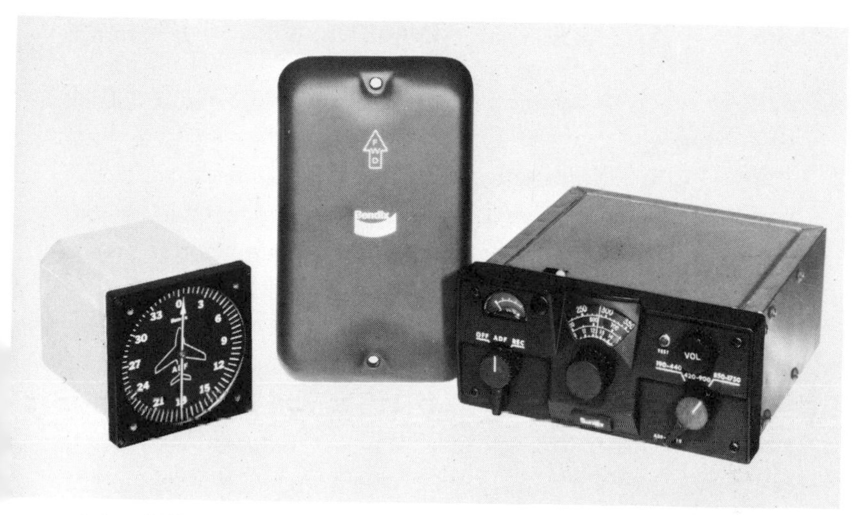

9.5 ADF receiver. The indicator at left points the station bearing with respect to the airplane. "0" is straight ahead, "9" is off the right wing, and so on.

COURTESY OF BENDIX AVIONICS DIVISION

cons in the U.S. for this purpose, but the ADF can "home" on any low-frequency radio facility, including the radio station in your town.

One of the problems with ADF is interference by lightning. As it flashes across the sky, lightning sends out low-frequency radio waves that you hear as annoying static on the AM radio in your home or car. We turn off the radio or switch it to FM when the static becomes too great in the summertime, but the ADF must still listen to all this and try to hear the signal it needs. If the lightning interference is stronger than the signal that an ADF is receiving, the needle may point the way into the thunderstorm! Although the pilot is not likely to be fooled by this, it does mean that he might have difficulty navigating when thunderstorms are numerous. But when the weather is good, the pilot can fly along, listening to music or to a news broadcast, with the ADF needle pointing the way straight across the countryside toward the station to which he is listening.

Most of the disadvantages of the low-frequency electronic navigation systems have been eliminated in the newest system, called *Very high frequency Omnidirectional Range* (or VOR). About one thousand VOR stations have literally put electronic highways in the sky everywhere over the U.S. Almost anywhere over the United States, a pilot can twirl the knobs of his VOR receiver and find his position on a navigation chart in a matter of seconds. The VOR uses Very High Frequency (VHF) radio waves, which are almost unaffected by atmospheric disturbances such as lightning. But these short waves travel only in straight lines. The airplane must therefore be "in sight" of a VOR station to receive it. When the airplane is on the ground, a station only a few miles away may be "out of sight" over the horizon. But as the airplane climbs to higher altitudes, it can "see" a much larger area of the earth's surface. An airplane a mile in the air can easily receive stations fifty to one hundred miles away.

The operating principle of the VOR is quite simple, although the equipment in the black box on the panel is somewhat complicated and expensive. Imagine a lighthouse that has two lights, one a *fixed* light which you can see from whereever you might be located around the station, the other a *rotating* light, like a searchlight, that can be seen only when it points in your direction. Let's assume that the fixed light flashes and then goes out, and that when it flashes, the rotating light starts at north and rotates its finger of light clockwise around through east, south, west, and back to north again in 10 seconds. With a stopwatch you can measure the time between the flash of the fixed light and the passage of the rotating light. If the elapsed time is 5 seconds, you know that the rotating light has moved halfway around and is pointing *south* when you see it. By timing the two flashes, you have found that you are exactly south of the station. If you measured 2½ seconds between flashes, you know that the rotating light has moved only a quarter of the way around when it strikes you, and you are *east* of the station.

The VOR operates, of course, with VHF radio waves rather than light rays, and the electronic equipment in the receiver automatically measures the time, does all the arithmetic for you, and provides the needed information on a simple instrument dial (figure 9.6). The pilot tunes the station by setting the radio dials on the right to its frequency, making sure that he has the right station by listening to its code call letters. He then sets the *course selector* to the course he wants "to" or "from" a station and follows the instructions of the "needle." When he is on the course he has selected, the needle will move to the center. The sketches in figure 9.7 show how a VOR indicator tells a pilot when he is on course or off course.

On any line through the VOR station the needle will center for two settings of the course selector. For example, on the line drawn through 60°-240° in figure 9.7, the needle will give an "on course" indication with the selector set at either 60° or 240°. An automatic flag will give a TO or FROM indication to tell the pilot whether his course-selector setting is a course toward or away from the station. Thus, on the 240° radial at the left of the figure, the needle is shown centered for 240° FROM or 60° TO, since these are simply two ways the

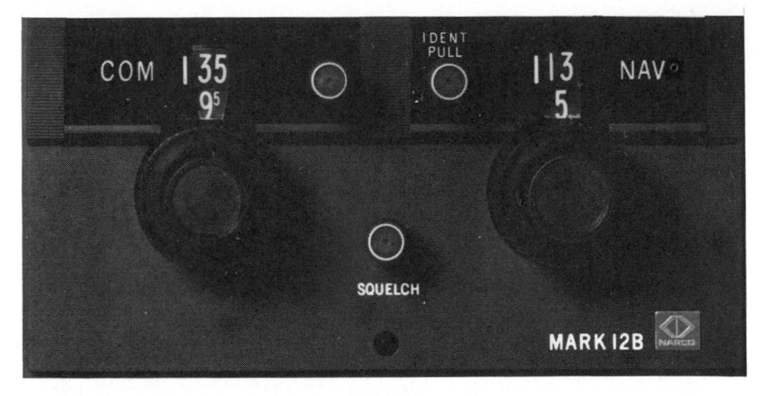

9.6 The VOR receiver (above) provides both communication (left dial) and navigation (right dial). The needle on the indicator (below) hangs vertically when the airplane is located on the radial selected, swings right or left to indicate direction in which airplane's course should be corrected.

COURTESY OF NARCO AVIONICS

COURTESY OF BENDIX AVIONICS DIVISION

pilot might fly this same radial. The TO or FROM flags do not tell the pilot which way he is flying. They tell him only his *position* with respect to the station.

An airplane can fly inbound on one radial (for example the 180° radial in figure 9.7), fly over the station and continue away from it on the same course. The flag automatically changes from TO to FROM as the station is passed. Or the pilot can reset the course selector to a different radial (for example 030°) when the station is passed, and fly outbound on that radial. Using VOR, the pilot can fly any established airway, or can create a new airway that goes where he wants to go by setting its course into the course selector.

Although the VOR receiver will tell the pilot his bearing (direction) from a station, it will not tell him how far away he is. He knows only that he is somewhere *on that bearing line.* If he can measure a second bearing from a different station, he can find his position exactly.

For example, let's assume that while flying in Arkansas we pass over a town, but are not sure what town it is. We tune Little Rock VOR, center the needle and read 202° FROM on the course selector; then tune Pine Bluff and read 273° FROM. We are somewhere on *both* the LIT 202° and the PBF 273° radials as shown in figure 9.8. These lines can intersect at only one point — our location. If we draw these two lines on a sectional chart (in figure 9.1, just place a strip of paper along each bearing) we will find that the town below us is SHERIDAN.

The pilot can find his distance from the station in miles without even looking at a map if he has *distance-measuring equipment,* or DME. The DME equipment in the airplane transmits a radio signal which is received by equipment at the VOR station on the ground. This signal causes the ground

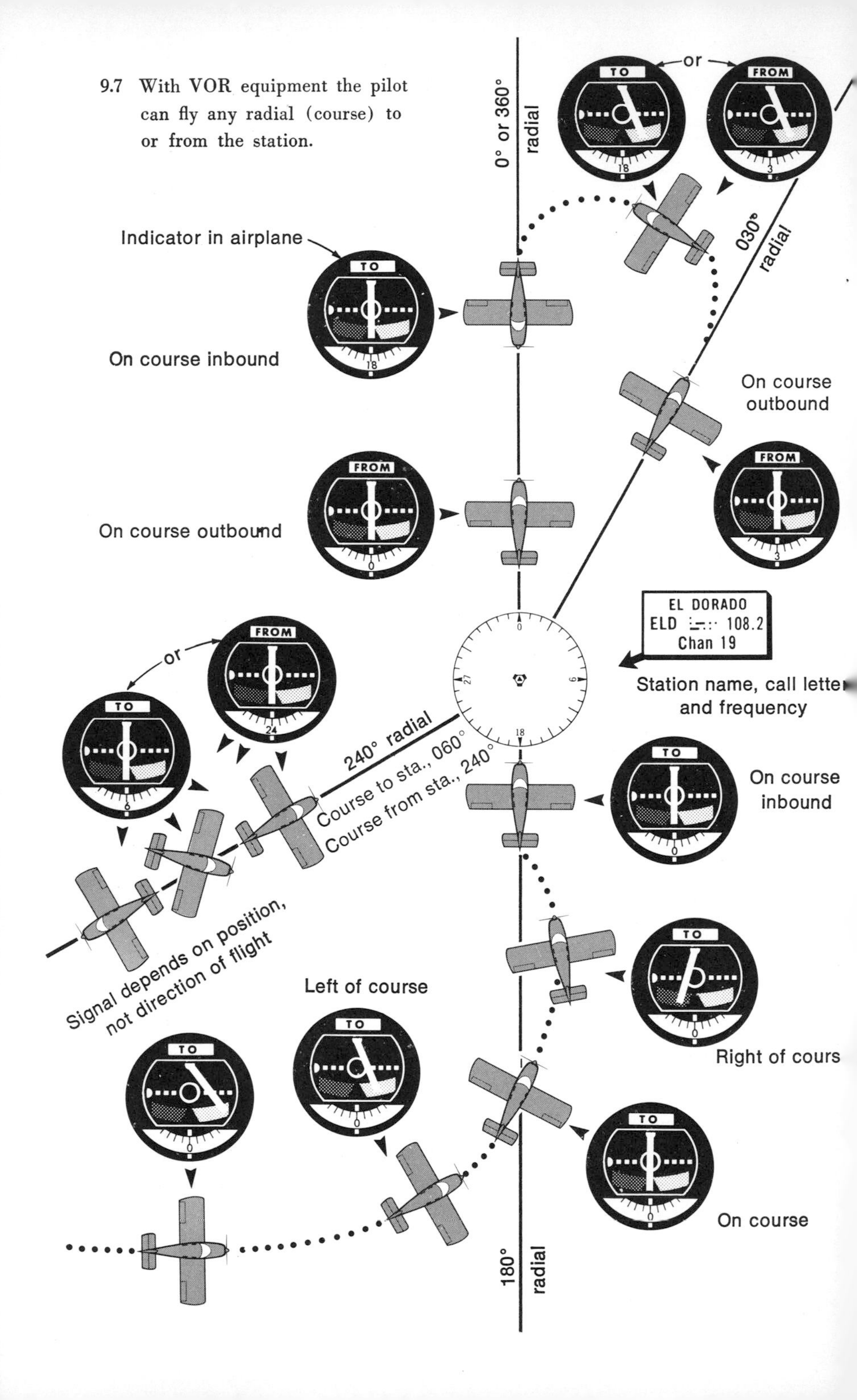

9.7 With VOR equipment the pilot can fly any radial (course) to or from the station.

station to send a radio signal back to the aircraft. The equipment in the airplane measures the time delay between the transmitted and received signals and converts this time measurement into a distance reading on the instrument dial. DME thus is like radar, except that it measures the time not between a transmitted and reflected signal but between a transmitted and a "triggered" answer. The time intervals that it must measure are extremely small. Radio waves travel at about 186,000 miles per second, yet DME equipment can measure accurately the time for the waves to travel only a few miles.

With VOR and other electronic aids, the problem of navigation becomes easier and easier, depending upon how much equipment the pilot can afford to buy and carry aboard his aircraft. Two separate VOR receivers are standard equipment on large aircraft, and are carried on many small airplanes. The second receiver gives the pilot added safety in case of failure of the first.

One last cockpit black box might be mentioned. This device, called the *course coupler,* connects the left-right signal of the VOR indicator into the automatic pilot to steer the airplane along any electronic (VOR) highway. If the VOR needle swings to the left, the autopilot is commanded to steer to the left until the needle is again centered. After tuning all his electronics, instructing them all properly, and switching on the autopilot, the pilot who has all this gear can just sit back, hands off, and watch his airplane fly and navigate itself to its destination.

With all this automatic gear, one might think that today's pilots need to know less about navigation that the old "iron-compass" pilot. Not so — the pilot must know how to use all

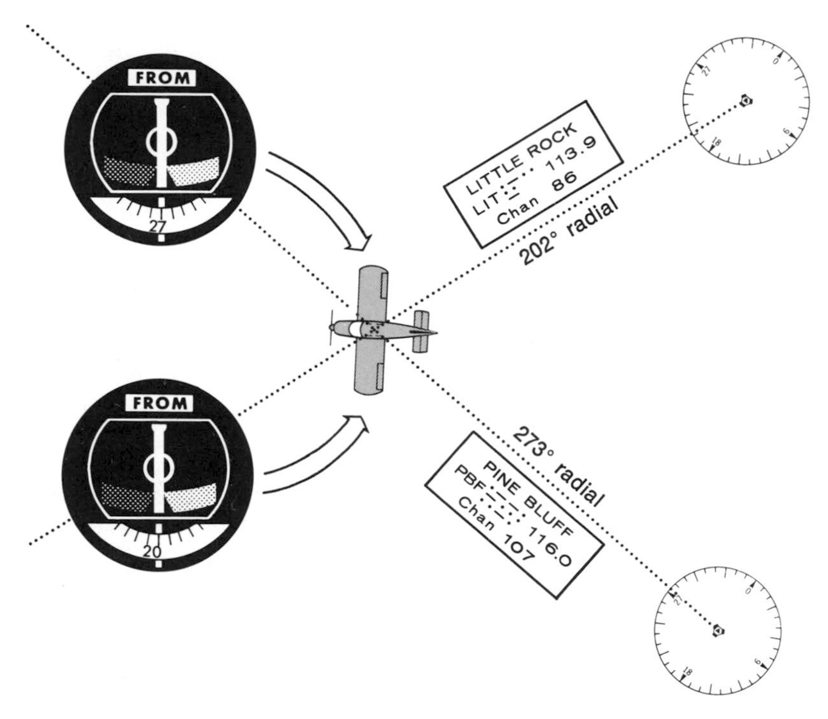

9.8 Locating your position by VOR. Tune two stations, turn course selector to center the needle, read the bearing from each station. Drawing the two radials on the chart (figure 9.1) will give location of airplane.

this equipment and must also be able to take over control from his black boxes at any time, if one of them should fail. Automatic navigation gear does relieve the pilot of the routine chores of flying and navigation so that he can spend his time on other problems. With airplanes traveling ever higher and faster, the pilot needs all the help he can get. But if he needs to, he still must be able to find his way with chart, pencil, and protractor, just as in the old days.

10

Which Way Is Up?

"CHEROKEE 95 JULIET is two miles from the outer marker, cleared for an approach. Contact Hobby Tower 118.7 outer marker inbound." With these cryptic words, Houston Approach Control has cleared us for an instrument approach to Hobby Airport at Houston.

Under the solid layer of clouds beneath our airplane lies the airport, invisible except to our instruments. When an instrument on our panel tells us that we are over the "outer marker," a radio beacon a few miles from the airport, we swing on to the approach path indicated by another instrument and begin the descent.

"Hobby Tower, Cherokee 95 Juliet is passing the outer marker inbound."

"Roger, Cherokee 95 Juliet. Continue approach."

As we leave the world above, the clouds close in around us like a dense fog. We can see neither earth nor sky, and we do not know which way is up or down. But our instruments know, and we watch them carefully, scanning rapidly from one to another in order to get all the information we need, moving the controls to make the airplane follow our invisible path down through the clouds. We begin to catch fleeting glimpses of the ground, then we suddenly break out of the clouds into the world below. Straight ahead lies the runway, right where it should be for landing.

"Cherokee 95 Juliet has the runway in sight," we tell the tower.

"95 Juliet is cleared to land, runway three."

These few minutes "on instruments" and the thousands of hours flown each day through fog, clouds, rain, or snow by all kinds of airplanes would be impossible without special instruments for the airplane and special training for the pilot.

Too much weight and too little muscle keep man from flying by his own power, but these are not his only deficiencies. He cannot fly by his own senses when he cannot see the ground. The *FAA Instrument-Flying Handbook* puts it this way: "Your body is not designed for flight. You are equipped to operate as a ground animal, . . . adapted to movement on the ground through sensory systems that you react to through habit."

The word "ground" here is important. Our remarkable system of balance works for us only when we know where the ground is. This system, located in what we call the "inner ear," makes possible all sorts of complicated activities that we take for granted: walking, riding a bicycle, skiing on water or snow. But our sense of balance that serves us well on the ground can be completely fooled in an airplane. If you cannot see the ground or the horizon, you have nothing by which to steer. You have no way of telling whether you are climbing or descending, no reference by which to level your wings to keep from turning.

If you close your eyes and lean while sitting in a chair, you can feel yourself leaning. If you go too far, the force of gravity, which always acts down toward the center of the earth, will upset the chair and pull you to the floor. If the same sensations were available in flight there would be no problem. But when an airplane *turns* it is *banked,* and the lift force that supports the airplane and you banks with it to remain perpendicular to the wings. The force the airplane exerts on the seat of your pants is therefore always straight up through your body (see figure 3.10) and gives you no "leaning" sensation whatever. Under conditions where you can't see the ground, you simply cannot tell the difference between straight-and-level flight, a gentle turn, or a steep spiral dive. All would "feel" the same.

You might think that your inner ear could detect the turning motion, but it cannot. It can detect only quick changes in attitude, such as you would feel if you sat on a swiveling piano stool and someone suddenly started you turning. But if you were blindfolded and the stool turned so quietly that you could get no hint from your eyes or ears, your speed could be changed very slowly and you would shortly have no idea whether you were still turning or not. Slow changes in attitude, which occur continually in airplane flight, are quite beyond the ability of your inner ear to detect.

Old-time pilots used to talk of flying "by the seat of their pants," and before the days of blind-flying instruments, they sometimes had to try to do just that when caught in fog or bad weather. Many pilots proved with their lives that it can't be done. As a ground animal, man does not naturally possess the equipment to tell which way is up when he cannot see the ground.

Today all commercial airlines, all military airplanes, and most smaller airplanes have instruments that enable a pilot to keep his airplane right-side-up and on course even when he can see nothing but the clouds or fog around him. He must be highly trained to use these instruments, and must pass a test for a special license before he can fly under "instrument conditions." This special license is called an *instrument rating* and the conditions under which instrument flight is conducted is called IFR, shorthand for *Instrument Flight Rules.*

The instruments that the pilot uses for instrument flight are not at all complicated if you relate them, one by one, to the simple basic maneuvers described in Chapter 8. Each instrument tells the pilot about at least one particular attitude or condition, and most instruments give him information on several conditions.

The three basic instruments that are used in learning to fly — the altimeter, the airspeed indicator, and the compass — are as vital for instrument flight as they are for visual flight. With the airspeed indicator we can adjust our speed for climb, glide, or cruise; with the altimeter we can hold a certain altitude; and with the compass we can hold a course in a certain direction. But when the horizon disappears and we can't see the ground, how can we hold the wings level?

If the wings are not level, the airplane will turn. We might therefore expect that we could keep the airplane from turning by reading the compass and holding a constant heading. The trouble is that the compass sloshes around in rough air, spins the wrong way when we turn in some directions, turns faster than the airplane under some conditions, and generally makes itself useless except under calm, steady conditions. The compass can't be counted on to show us accurately whether we are turning or not. The instrument we need was invented in 1918, and immediately began to save the lives of pilots who suddenly found themselves trapped in clouds or fog. The gyroscopic turn indicator, now called the turn-and-slip indicator, used a gyroscope to detect a turning motion. The gyro (to use its nickname) operates on the same principle as the toy gyroscopes with which most of us are familiar. The spinning wheel of the gyro tends to keep its axle pointed in the same direction at all times (see figure 7.7). When the airplane turns, the gyro is forced to point its axis in another direction. Because the gyro is mounted on springs, its resistance to being turned deflects a needle on a dial. If the pilot operates the airplane controls to keep the needle centered, he knows that he is not turning and that his wings must therefore be level. On the other hand, when he wishes to turn, he can bank the airplane to deflect the needle to the rate of turn he desires. For example, the turn-and-slip indicator in the illustration shows a mark on the dial for a "2-minute turn." When the pilot banks the airplane to move the needle to the mark, the airplane will turn through a full circle in just two minutes.

The turn indicator was perhaps the most important single instrument invention in all of aviation. Over forty years ago it was first put to work in the very dangerous business of flying the mail. An airmail pilot caught in fog or storm did not have enough instruments to find the airport for a safe landing. But with the turn indicator he could fly "blind" to where the weather might be better, or could at last resort climb to a safe altitude where he could jump from the airplane to parachute safely to the ground. Without the turn indicator the pilot caught in fog was usually doomed to lose control and crash.

When aviation began to move seriously toward "blind flying" or what is now known as *instrument flight,* it was recognized that better instruments would be needed to achieve the desired precision. What the pilot needed most, when he couldn't see the real horizon, was an *artificial horizon.* And

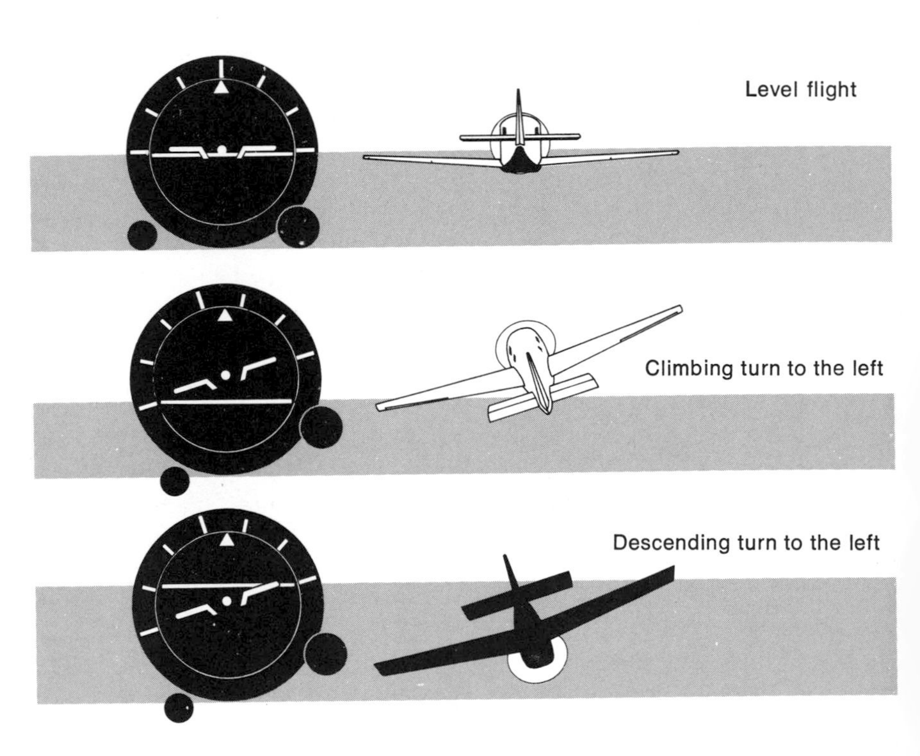

10.1 The artificial horizon or attitude indicator

that's exactly what the most important blind-flying instrument is called. Another name for it is *attitude indicator,* which is a more accurate term. The useful little gyro is the basis for this instrument. The gyro is mounted in a system of pivots that permit it to keep its axis pointing in the same direction no matter what maneuvers the airplane goes through. The gyro "remembers" where the horizon is, and shows the pilot a tiny "airplane" and a "horizon" (figure 10.1). When the real airplane banks, the tiny airplane on the instrument face banks too, showing the pilot what he would see if the real horizon were visible. Angle marks on the dial make it possible to bank the airplane more precisely when flying on instruments than when flying without. When the pilot dives or climbs his airplane, the tiny airplane on the instrument moves below or above the "horizon." Thus, on this one key instrument the pilot can see displayed all of his attitudes: bank, climb, and glide.

The other instrument that was badly needed for precision instrument flight was a substitute for the sloshy, erratic compass — a steady instrument to steer by. Again the useful little gyro came to the rescue, and made possible the *directional gyro* or DG. The DG uses a gyro mounted on pivots to show changes in the airplane's direction of travel (figure 10.2). It has heading marks in degrees, like a compass, but it doesn't swing around or have any of the other bad habits of the compass. The DG just keeps pointing in the same direction no matter where the airplane turns. But there's one problem — the DG has not the faintest idea which *direction* it is pointing. So the pilot must read the compass when it is quiet and set the DG dial to the correct magnetic heading. The pilot then has a steady magnetic heading to steer by.

The gyro always keeps its axis pointing in the same direction, but we must remember that this "same direction" means with regard to *space*. As the earth turns on its axis, and as the airplane travels, the gyro keeps pointing in the same direction in *space*, not in the same direction on the earth's surface. The motion of the earth, friction in the bearings supporting the gyro, and other factors therefore introduce errors into the DG's setting, and the pilot must set the instrument to agree with the compass every half hour or so.

Some large airplanes have a *remote compass*, which is much steadier than the liquid compass. A sensitive device,

10.2 The directional gyro (two styles)

often located in the wing, feels the earth's magnetic field and sends an electrical signal to drive a compass indicator on the pilot's panel. This equipment is sometimes used to automatically keep the DG set to agree with the remote compass.

The panel we need to "fly instruments" is almost complete — only one more is needed: the *vertical-speed indicator,* sometimes called the *rate-of-climb indicator.* Both the sealed case and the inside of the diaphragm of this simple instrument (figure 10.3) contains "static pressure." The pressure tube carrying this pressure to the inside of the diaphragm has a constriction that delays the flow through it. In level flight the pressure in both the case and the diaphragm are the same, and the instrument dial reads "0." When the altitude is changing, the pressure changes immediately in the outer case of the instrument, but less rapidly inside the diaphragm because of the lag caused by the constriction. A pressure difference therefore exists across the diaphragm, tending to either squeeze it to a flatter shape or to puff it up to a less-flat shape, depending upon whether the higher pressure is inside or outside the diaphragm. The more rapid the change of altitude, the larger the pressure difference. The movement of the diaphragm is geared to the instrument dial where a moving hand tells the pilot whether his airplane is going up or down, and how fast.

The pilot can also learn from his altimeter whether the airplane is climbing or descending, but the vertical-speed indicator gives him a more sensitive indication and makes it possible for him to accurately execute a change of altitude. If the pilot is ordered by Air Traffic Control to descend 10,000 feet in ten minutes, for example, he adjusts his flight path so that the vertical-speed indicator hand points to "1" in the "down" direction. The airplane will descend at a rate of 1,000 feet per minute and complete the descent in the time allotted.

By now you probably have noticed that there's some duplication on the panel. Both the altimeter and the vertical-speed indicator tell the pilot of changing altitude. The attitude indicator, too, tells him when his airplane is in a climb or glide. Changing airspeed would also tell him. The attitude indicator tells him when he is banking, while the turn indicator tells

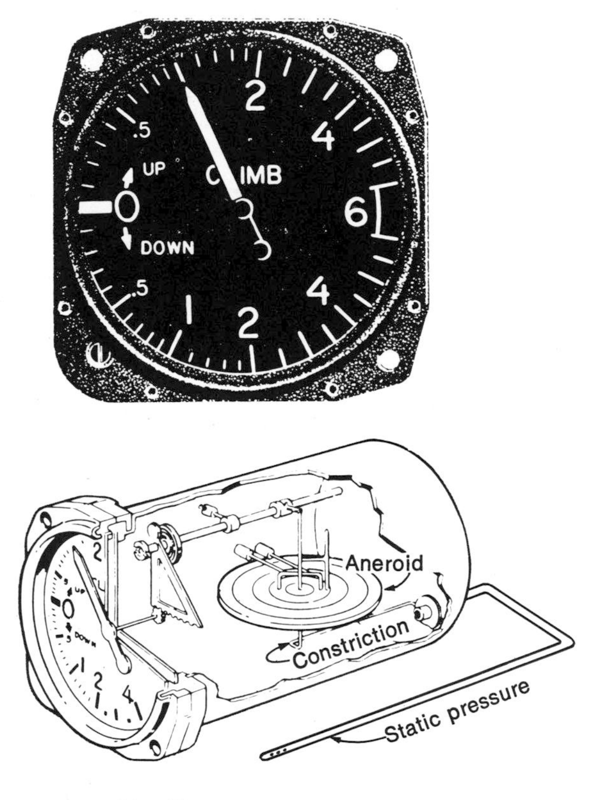

10.3 The vertical-speed indicator
COURTESY OF FEDERAL AVIATION AGENCY

him when he is turning, which is the same thing. The DG also tells him when he's turning.

These duplications give the pilot a constant check on the operation of his instruments. If one disagrees with the rest, it may have failed. If it has failed, the pilot has the others to fall back on. To give further protection, the instruments may be driven by different methods. The attitude indicator and DG may be driven by a vacuum pump attached to the engine, while the turn indicator may be electrically driven. A failure of one system leaves the other still operating, and gives the pilot the means for completing his flight safely. Large multi-engined airplanes generally have two complete sets of flight instruments, one in front of the pilot and one in front of the copilot, for added safety.

The six instruments mounted together in figure 10.4 should look like old friends to you by now. With them, and with a compass and an engine tachometer, you are ready for an instrument flight. Each of the three parts of the illustration shows how the flight instruments would look with the airplane in a different maneuver. See if you can describe the attitude of the airplane in each case.

How long did it take you? Probably longer than the pilot could afford to use while flying on instruments. Because the airplane is in motion and things are constantly changing, the pilot must have, in addition to the instruments, the skill to use them rapidly and continuously. He must *scan* his instruments — that is, look quickly and briefly at first one and then another — in proper order, making decisions and appropriate control deflection as his eye moves along.

It sounds complicated, and it has been likened to juggling three or four tennis balls in the air at one time. But if we recall the way we learned to recognize and control airplane attitude during the basic maneuvers described in Chapter 3, it becomes a step-by-step process that is much more simple. Pilots disagree among themselves on the order in which one should scan the panel, but let's try a round as it might be done. Let's say we're flying straight and level on instruments on a heading of 0° at 5,000 feet. (You will have to imagine the following changes from what is shown in the first sketch of figure 10.4.) The artificial horizon shows the wings level, but the dot has moved slightly below the bar, indicating a slight dive. A glance at the altimeter and vertical-speed indicators confirms this. Give the wheel a momentary bit of back pressure and move your eyes to the DG. The DG says you're a little to the left of our heading. Turn the wheel slightly to the right for a few seconds to put the airplane in a shallow right turn, then wheel neutral again. Check the artificial horizon. Move your eyes quickly to the vertical-speed indicator. It says you're not climbing or descending, so on to the altimeter. The altimeter says that you're now a little high. Put a forward pressure on the wheel for a moment and move your eyes to the artificial horizon. It says you're still in a slight right turn. Move on to the DG. It says you're back on course, so move aileron to left to level wings. Move to the horizon . . . and so on. This exercise might have taken a minute or so to run through in print, but the pilot might complete the whole thing in a few seconds on his panel.

By moving rapidly from one instrument to another, making small needed corrections *without waiting to see what happens,* you can keep all errors small and fly an accurate course. But if you keep staring at one instrument while you move the airplane's controls to make it read right, all the other attitudes

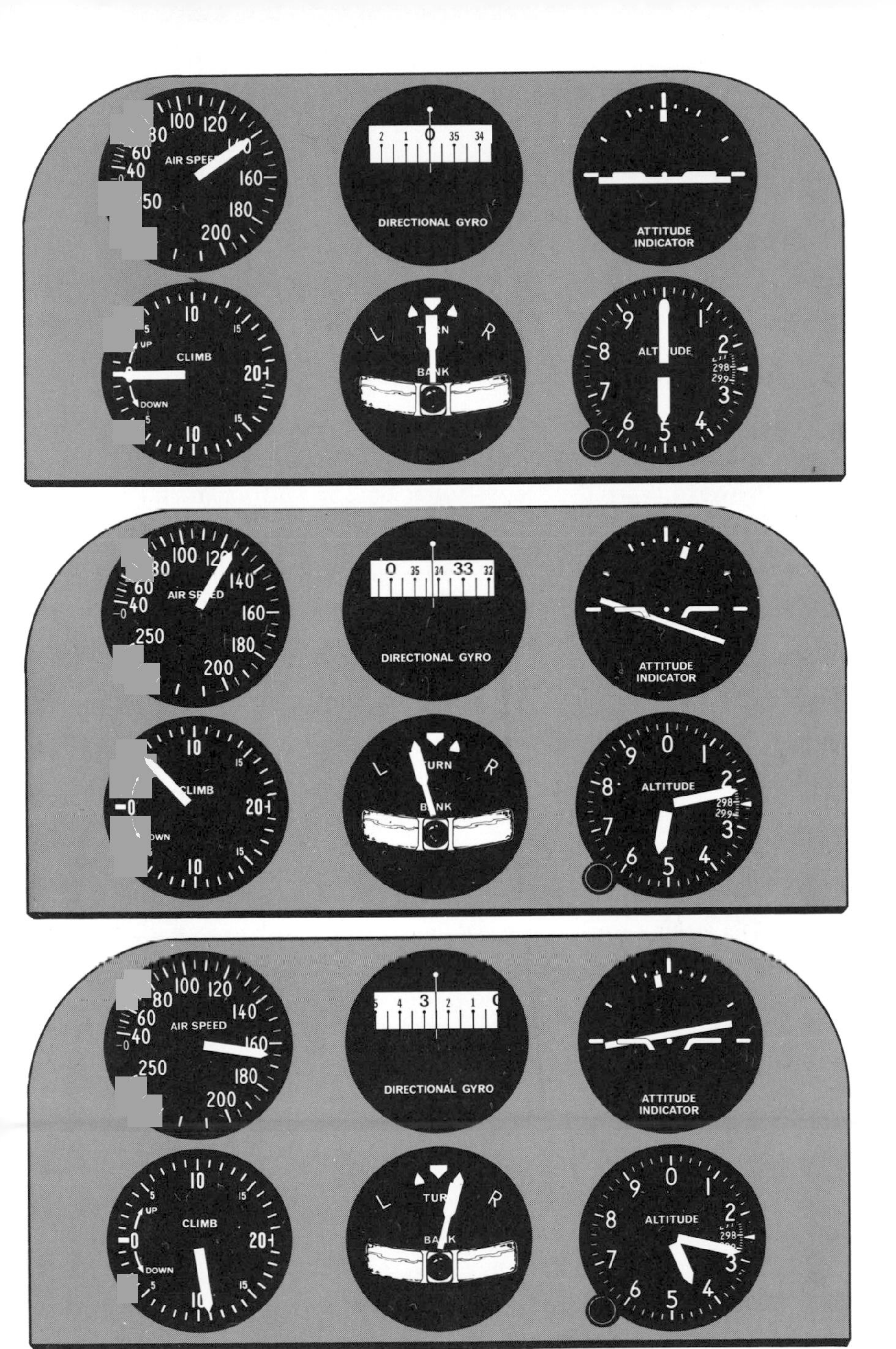

10.4 What airplane altitude is indicated by each of these instrument-panel drawings?

of the airplane will likely get way off. By the time you have stared at the next one and corrected it, the one you just straightened out will be off again, and the airplane will wander and wallow around the sky. In juggling four balls, if you concentrate too long on any one, the rest will surely fall.

Somewhere in the scan of the four instruments described above, the pilot must shoot an occasional glance at engine power, engine speed, airspeed, the turn-and-slip indicator, and at his navigation instruments. The instrument pilot is a very busy fellow. If the airplane has an autopilot, this can take some of the load off him. But he must still be able to take over and do it all himself when necessary. Each individual operation of instrument flying is rather simple, like the individual basic maneuvers of flying. But putting them all together, like putting the basic maneuvers together, takes training and practice.

Besides learning to scan and to interpret the instruments and make the necessary control corrections, it is absolutely necessary that the pilot learn to ignore — *totally ignore* — his own ideas and feelings about the attitude of the airplane. The pilot's ground-animal equipment can become confused and give him a strong feeling that he is leaning or turning one way or another. Occasional glimpses of the ground or breaks in the clouds can create an illusion that the attitude of the airplane is different from what the instruments describe. If the pilot allows himself to believe any of this false information, he is in grave danger of becoming disoriented and losing control of the airplane. Only his instruments know which way is up, and he must discipline himself to believe and to follow them completely. When he learns to do this, he is no longer just a ground animal, but has become a sky animal as well, able to operate out of sight of his earth in the topsy-turvy world of the clouds.

How does a pilot learn to fly solely by means of instruments? He can learn only by doing exactly that. The horizon, clouds, and the ground must be hidden from his view so that he will learn to rely completely upon his instruments. It would not be practical to use foggy days or the inside of clouds for practicing instrument flying, so other ways have been devised. The pilot may wear a "hood" which blocks out his view of everything but the instrument panel. Or he may wear goggles of colored glass and cover the windshield with plastic of another color, which would let him see the panel but not the outside world. An instructor must ride beside him, of course, to keep a watch for other airplanes as well as to instruct the student.

On the other hand, the pilot may learn instrument flying in a "flight simulator" in an air-conditioned classroom without ever leaving the ground. The first flight simulator was invented by Edwin A. Link in 1929, soon after instrument flying began. Many kinds of simulators have been used in the training of thousands of personal, professional, and military pilots since that time.

The part of the simulator that the pilot sees is the cockpit (figure 10.5), which is built just like the cockpit of the type of airplane it is supposed to simulate. The flight controls, flight instruments, engine instruments, and navigational gear look like those found on instrument panels everywhere, but the instruments don't operate like those described in an earlier chapter, because this "airplane" doesn't really fly. Instead the instruments are driven by a computer, and they tell the pilot what the machine *would* do in response to his control motions if it were an airplane instead of a simulator.

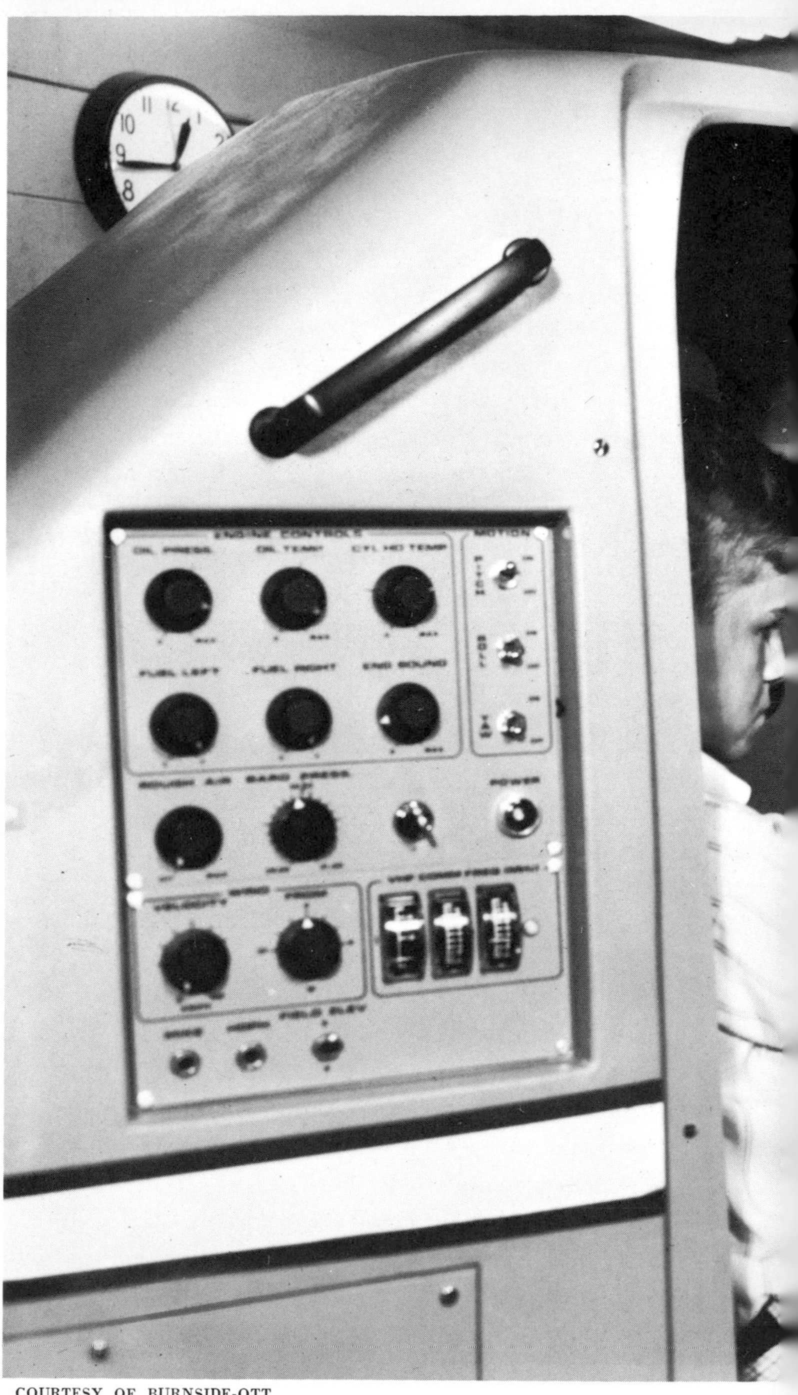

COURTESY OF BURNSIDE-OTT

10.5 Learning instrument flying in a flight simulator

With the door closed and the windows covered to simulate instrument flight, the pilot experiences a strong illusion that he is actually in flight. The engine sound changes when the throttle position or airplane attitude is changed, the simulator may (if it is built with this feature) bank as it turns or tilt up or down as it climbs or glides. And, of course, the instruments respond exactly as they would on a real airplane.

The part of the simulator that the pilot does not see is the heart of the device, a computer. It is the computer that makes the simulator behave as though it were an airplane. In a real airplane, moving the wheel back will cause the airplane to nose-up, lose speed, and climb, depending upon the throttle setting. The airplane responds according to its speed, weight, power setting, and so on, according to the laws of gravity and mechanics. In the simulator, the computer takes the wheel (elevator) position, throttle setting, altitude, and so forth, and calculates what the airplane in flight would do. The results of these calculations are automatically placed on the flight instruments on the simulator panel. If the controls are moved for climb, for example, the vertical-speed indicator will move to the calculated "rate-of-climb," the altimeter will turn slowly toward a higher altitude, and the airspeed will decrease to the calculated climb speed. If the pilot moves the controls for a turn, the turn indicator will tell him how fast he is "turning," the artificial horizon will tell him his "bank angle," and even the slip indicator (the ball in the tube) will tell him if he is slipping or skidding his "turn." The compass and directional gyro will move as the "heading" of the simulator changes.

The radio and navigational equipment work, too, and the pilot can fly an "omni course" along an imaginary airway from one station to another. Precise instrument approaches

10.6 The computer plots the "flight path" of the simulator on the chart (foreground) while the instructor observes the student's performance. COURTESY OF SINGER LINK DIVISION

(to be described in the next chapter) can be made to any "airport" whose approach pattern has been placed in the computer. The pilot tunes his navigational equipment and follows its instructions just as he would in an airplane.

The computer draws a permanent record of the pilot's "flight path" by moving a pen along his course on an instrument chart, as shown in figure 10.6. The instructor can sit outside the cabin to observe and instruct; he can also play the role of the flight controller, issuing instructions and clearances to the student by "radio" just as airway control, approach control, or the control tower would in actual flight. From his control panel on the side of the trainer, the instructor can twist knobs to give the student "rough air," "wind" from any direction, or any number of "cockpit emergencies" such as low oil pressure, overheated engine, and so forth.

Many flying schools believe that first learning to fly a sim-

10.7 The runway seen through this windshield isn't really there. It's only a picture of a runway projected in front of a jet-transport simulator. Computer controlled, the runway image moves and changes to give the pilot the view he would have as he takes off in a real airplane. COURTESY OF SINGER LINK DIVISION

ulator helps a student to feel at home with controls and instruments, and makes learning to fly the real airplane easier and safer. Simulator training is valued so highly by the FAA that simulator time can be used to satisfy half of the minimum requirement of the forty hours of training required for an instrument rating. The other half, quite logically, must be performed in actual flight. The flight test itself, as you would expect, must be performed in an actual airplane.

The airlines and the militray services use simulators extensively for crew training. Large airplanes cost hundreds or even thousands of dollars per hour to operate. The expense of operating a simulator may be only a small fraction of this cost. Large simulators (for a four-engined jet transport, for example) are extremely complicated, and can train pilot, copilot, and flight engineer all at the same time. In fact, the skill of all three crew members is required to even get the "engines started" and to get the simulator "off the ground!" Some of the more sophisticated simulators for large airplanes have movies of the approaching airport projected on a screen in front of the windshield for the touchdown (figure 10.7). As the pilot prepares for his landing on the runway, the simulation is so realistic that he can scarcely tell that he is not flying the real thing. He can hear the sound of the retractable landing gear "going down" and hear it "clunk" as it locks in place. And if he finds himself expecting his wheels to "chirp" as they touch down on the runway, he won't be disappointed. The simulator does that, too.

11

"ATC Clears Cherokee November 8995 Juliet..."

WHEN YOU FLY an airplane "on instruments" through fog or clouds, you can't see other airplanes in time to avoid them. How can you be sure that there are no other airplanes in the airspace you will occupy?

The answer is that it's against federal law for you or anyone else to be up there in "instrument weather" except under very special conditions. Federal Air Regulations stipulate that:

> "No person may operate an aircraft in controlled airspace under Instrument Flight Rules (IFR) unless — (a) he has filed an IFR flight plan; and (b) he has received an appropriate Air Traffic Control (ATC) clearance."

The IFR *flight plan* is the pilot's request for use of controlled airspace, and the ATC *clearance* is his guarantee that the airspace is assigned to him alone. Regulations further stipulate that no one may file an IFR flight plan unless he is "instrument rated" and his airplane is properly equipped for instrument flight. This makes the instrument pilot a rather special person and instrument flight a very special kind of flight.

When a clearance is given to you for an instrument flight, the flight will be tightly controlled by ATC, using radio communications, all the way from takeoff to landing. The controller knows when you left the ground, how fast you are traveling, and relies upon you to tell him when you will arrive at your next checkpoint, usually the next omni (VOR) station. He blocks out for you alone a chunk of the sky along the airway as much as 100 miles long and 1,000 feet deep. He will generally assign you to an even altitude (6,000, 8,000, etc.) if you are westbound, or an odd altitude (5,000, 7,000, etc.) if you are eastbound. With traffic a thousand feet above and below you going in the opposite direction, you obviously must hold accurately to your assigned altitude. If one airplane is overtaking another at the same altitude, the controller may order one to a different altitude so that they can pass safely. In most parts of the country, particularly the heavily traveled areas, the controller will be watching all traffic in his area on a radarscope, and will tell you when he sees other airplanes that are headed in your direction.

If you are in good weather, say on top of the clouds, it is your responsibility to watch for and avoid other airplanes, even though you are in airspace assigned to you on an IFR flight plan. Other airplanes may use this airspace, too, because under *visual flight rules* (VFR) any airplane may fly in airspace where the ceiling and visibility make it safe to do so. Generally speaking, you may fly VFR anywhere the visibility is three miles or greater, provided that you are at least 500 feet below or 1,000 feet above and not less than 2,000 feet horizontally from any cloud. At high altitudes where airplane speeds are faster, you must have visibility of at least five miles and must stay even farther away from clouds. The thing to remember is that the airspace inside and near clouds is reserved for IFR traffic *only*, but the wide-open spaces between, above, and below clouds may be used by *both* kinds of traffic. Under these latter conditions, all pilots must be alert to avoid other airplanes on a see-and-be-seen basis.

We will see how these flight rules work and how the various controllers handle an IFR flight by flying IFR between Memphis and Little Rock shortly. First, we should look at a few important tools we will need on our instrument flight.

Although airways are shown on sectional charts like that in figure 9.1, there is not room for all of the extra information that the instrument pilot needs. Special charts, called *enroute* charts (or sometimes *RF* charts for "radio facility") are made which show him only airways and navigational (radio) facilities. No natural or man-made features of the terrain are illustrated except for principal airports and large bodies of water — oceans, bays, the Great Lakes, and so forth. A look at the portion of an enroute chart in figure 11.1 shows why. So much information is displayed that the features of the sectional chart could not be shown without making the whole thing impossible to read. The instrument pilot really doesn't need ground features on this chart anyway. On an instrument flight plan, he must navigate from airport to airport *entirely* by radio, and may not be able to see the ground at all. Actually, most instrument pilots will carry sectional charts in case they are needed in an emergency.

A closer look at the enroute charts shows that they are not as complex as they seem. The main features are the VOR (omni) stations and the airways that extend from them in all directions. The airways are numbered with a *V* (for Victor) number, and the compass bearing for each airway is shown at the circle around the VOR station, called the "compass rose." For example, the Victor 54 airway which we will be using has a compass bearing of 257° leaving Memphis. With our *omni-course selector* set on 257 and the needle centered, we will follow this highway in the sky to Little Rock. The distance between stations is shown in the little box as 111 (nautical) miles. Other numbers below the airway line show distances between intersections. The numbers above the airway designation show the minimum altitude at which this route can be flown for adequate terrain clearance (1,600 feet) and the minimum altitude at which one may fly and still receive the navigational facilities (2,500 feet). Low-frequency radio beacons are shown (for example, "Bruins" and "Forrest City") with their frequencies and the identification letters that we will hear in Morse code if we tune the station with our ADF. "Intersections" on the airways are shown as small triangles, and are named for identification, such as PORTER and BISCOE on V54. Some of these are actual intersections of two airways, but many are simply special "reporting points." With these points marked on their radarscopes, the controllers can identify a particular airplane by asking the pilot to report over a particular intersection.

Flying the airway from one city to the other will be easy. But how will we find our destination airport and the end of the runway with our instruments? The same omni equipment that brought us there, or our ADF equipment, or perhaps both, can be used for our "instrument approach." But we must know what

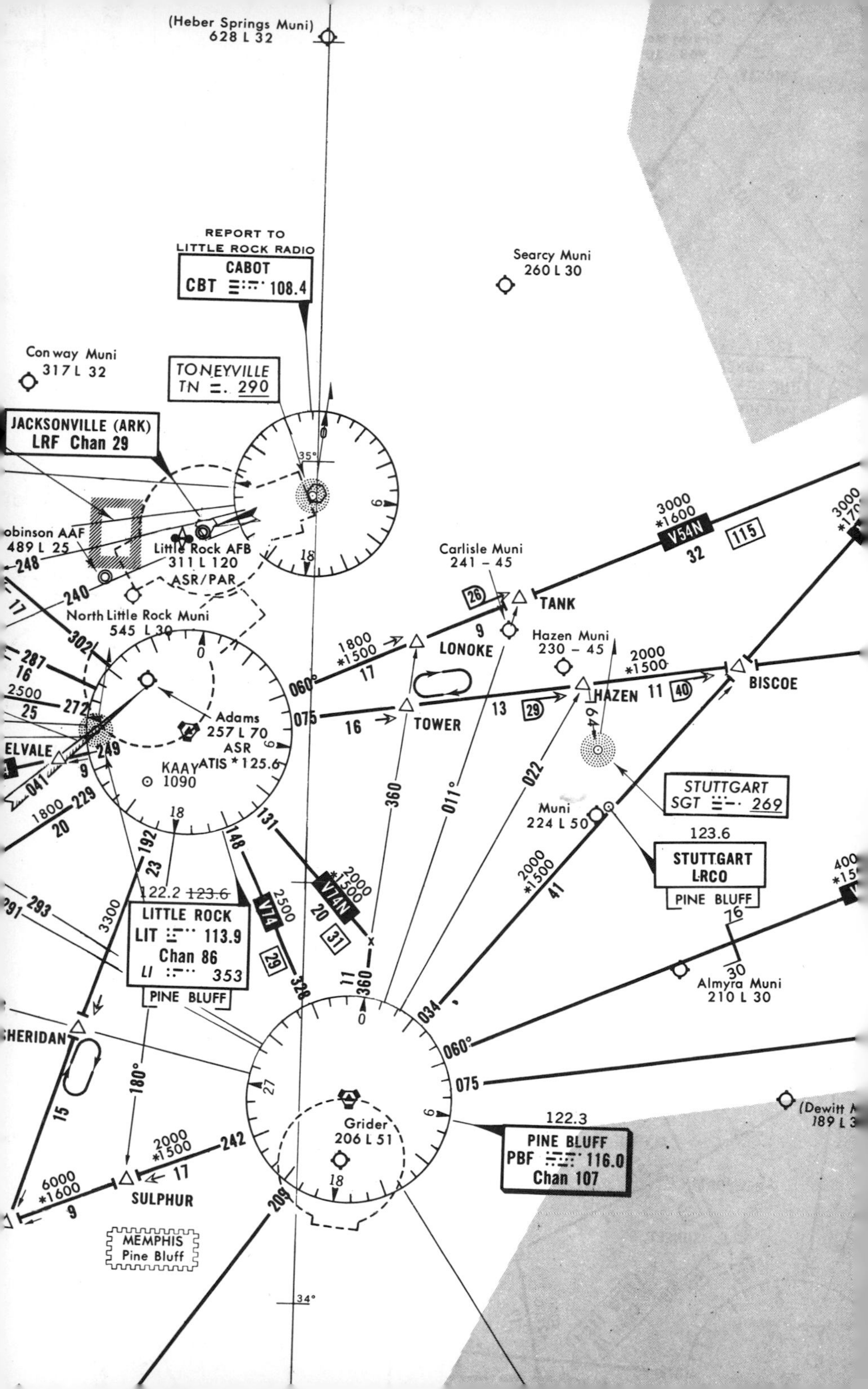

(Heber Springs Muni)
628 L 32
REPORT TO
LITTLE ROCK RADIO
CABOT
CBT 108.4
Searcy Muni
260 L 30
Con way Muni
317 L 32
TONEYVILLE
TN 290
JACKSONVILLE (ARK)
LRF Chan 29
35°
Robinson AAF
489 L 25
Little Rock AFB
311 L 120
ASR/PAR
North Little Rock Muni
545 L 30
3000
*1600
V54N
32
115
Carlisle Muni
241 – 45
26
TANK
1800
*1500
17
060°
9
LONOKE
Hazen Muni
230 – 45
2000
*1500
BISCOE
075
16
TOWER
13
29
HAZEN
11
40
Adams
257 L 70
ASR
ATIS *125.6
KAAY
1090
ELVALE
2500
25
1800
20
STUTTGART
SGT 269
Muni
224 L 50
123.6
STUTTGART
LRCO
PINE BLUFF
2000
*1500
41
122.2 123.6
LITTLE ROCK
LIT 113.9
Chan 86
LI 353
PINE BLUFF
3300
V74
2500
29
V14N
2000
*1500
20
31
Almyra Muni
210 L 30
SHERIDAN
180°
15
Grider
206 L 51
122.3
PINE BLUFF
PBF 116.0
Chan 107
(Dewitt
189 L 3
2000
*1500
17
6000
*1600
9
SULPHUR
MEMPHIS
Pine Bluff
34°

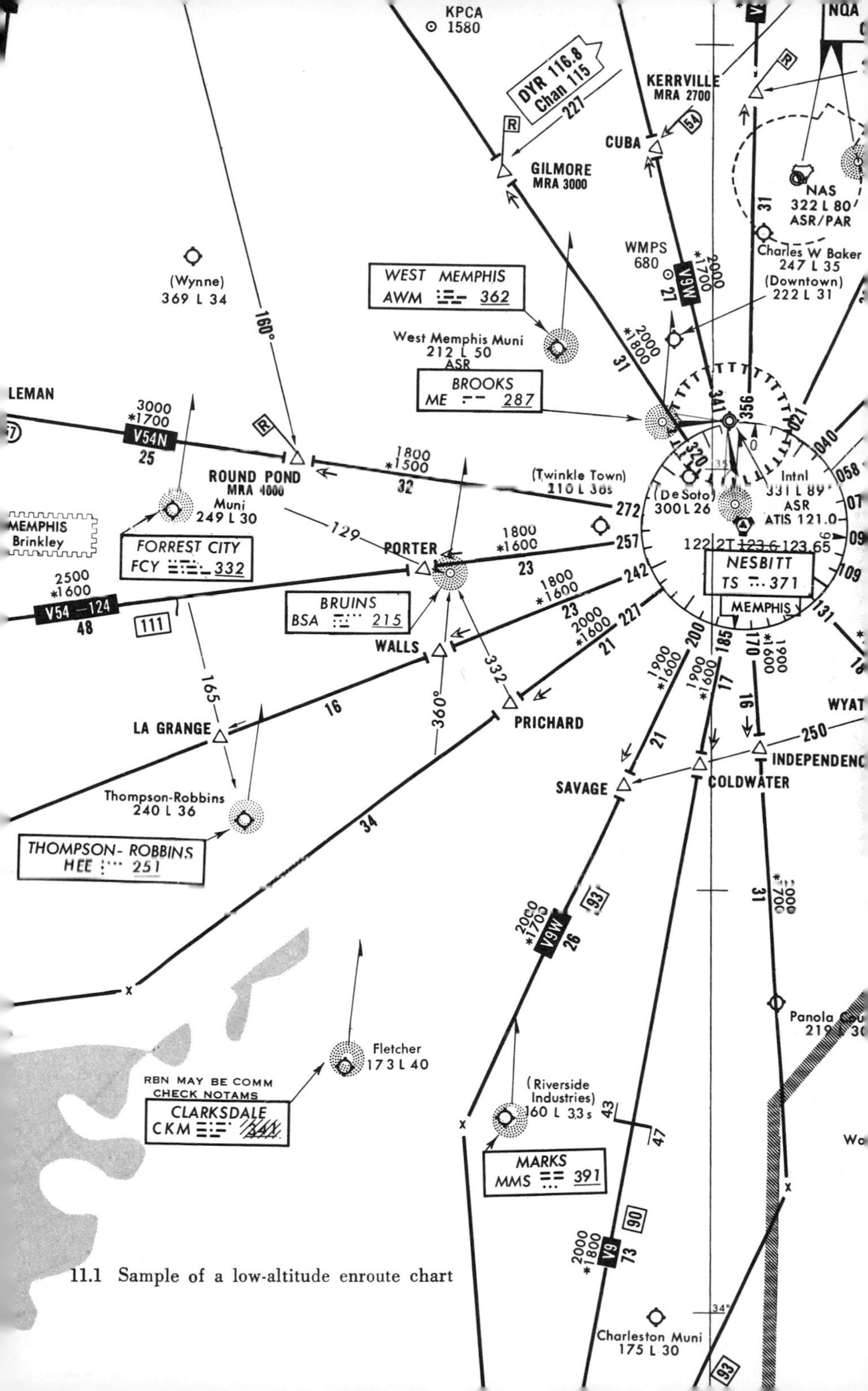

11.1 Sample of a low-altitude enroute chart

headings to fly, when to descend and to what altitude, in order to safely clear all obstacles and arrive at the end of the runway without being able to see it until we are almost upon it. We need another kind of chart, called an *instrument approach chart* or "approach plate" for short. This is a small, detailed chart that shows, first of all, the location of the airport and the radio facilities to be used in the instrument approach. The approach plate for Little Rock (Adams Field) (figure 11.2) shows in the upper sketch a complete *instrument landing system* (ILS) which has a "localizer," a "glide slope," an outer marker (OM), a middle marker (MM) (the lens-shaped areas on the localizer course) and a low-frequency beacon located at the OM. The Little Rock VOR is also shown, which is where the airway would bring the airplane to begin the approach. The localizer "final-approach" course starts at the lower left and cuts across the OM and MM to the airport runway.

The sketch at the lower left shows the minimum *altitudes* we need to have at the various points: 1,900 feet at the procedure turn, 1,900 feet at the OM, descending then to whatever minimum altitude is listed for the categories of airplanes shown in the table below the sketch. The sketch at the lower right shows the airport runways and the height of obstructions (the little tent-shaped symbols) located nearby. A lot of information on one small piece of paper!

The localizer is like a very sensitive VOR station. When the pilot tunes his omni receiver to the localizer frequency (110.3), the pointer on his instrument will center only when the airplane is on the very narrow final-approach path to the runway (figure 11.3). Accuracy is very important, because when a pilot breaks out of a very low overcast, he may have

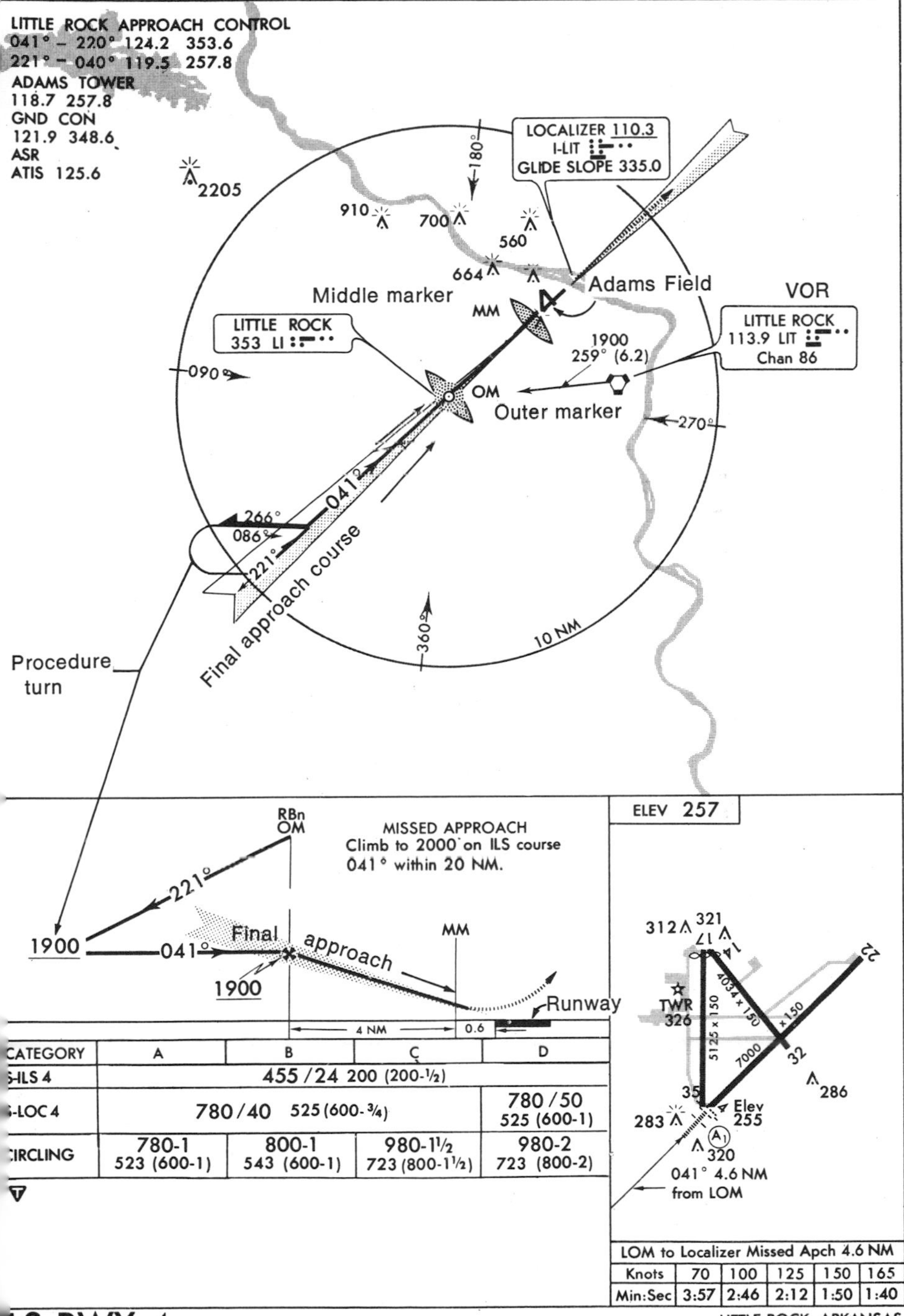

11.2 Typical instrument approach chart
(Some detail removed. Do not use for navigation.)

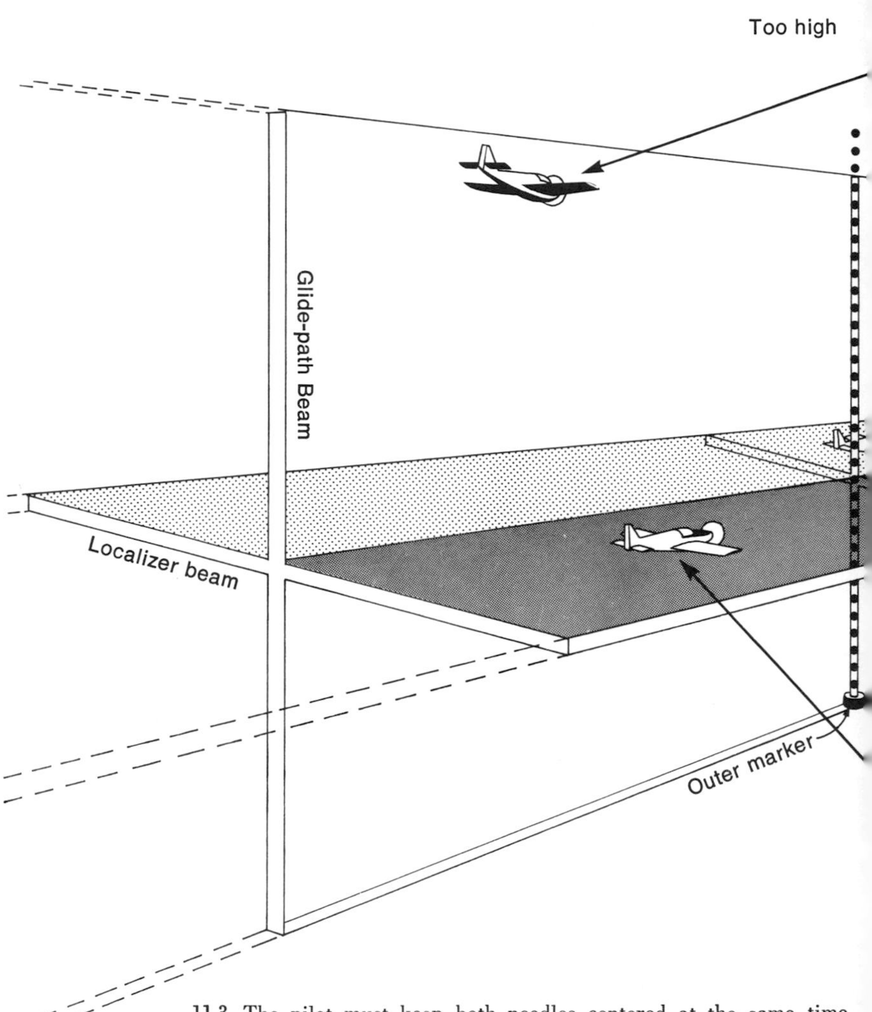

11.3 The pilot must keep both needles centered at the same time to stay on the approach path of the instrument landing system.

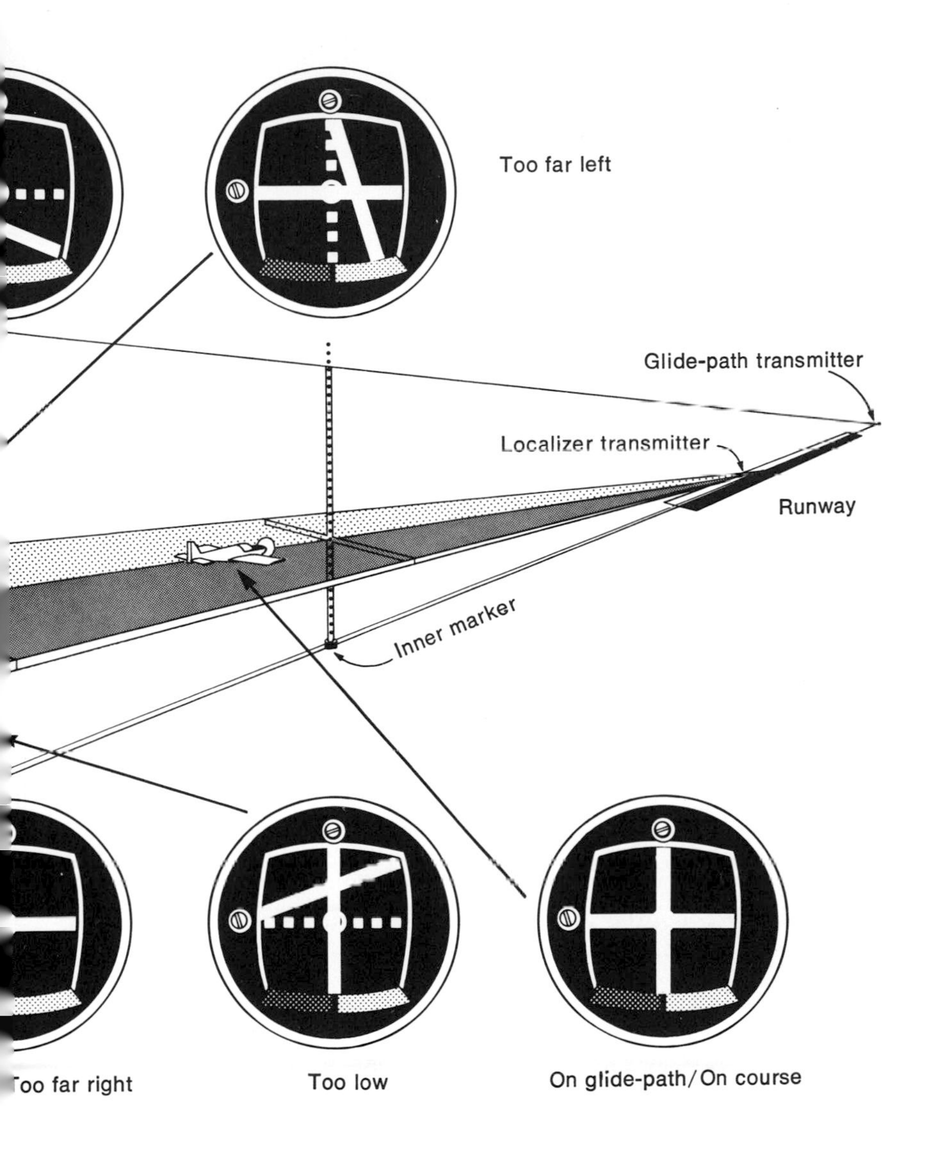
Too far left
Glide-path transmitter
Localizer transmitter
Runway
Inner marker
Too far right
Too low
On glide-path/On course

only a few seconds to maneuver and must be nicely lined up with the runway ready to land.

The glide slope is a second system that operates much like the localizer except that it gives the pilot an *altitude* path to follow. The horizontal needle on the omni indicator tells him when he is on, above, or below the correct path in his descent from the OM to the MM.

The outer and middle markers are short-range transmitters that can be heard only when the airplane is *directly over* them. The marker-beacon receiver in the airplane flashes a light and sounds a tone in the pilot's earphones (or cabin speaker) to tell him he is above one of these markers.

Now let's see how an approach is made on an instrument landing system. Inbound on the airway toward the VOR station, the pilot tunes and adjusts all his equipment. He must have everything ready — the required maneuvers come close together, and he must act quickly and almost automatically during the approach. Here is where training and experience count.

At the VOR, the pilot is cleared by ATC for an approach. You can follow his path on the approach plate (figure 11.2). He steers a course of 259° from the VOR toward the outer marker, 6.2 miles away. When his localizer indicator shows that he is approaching the course, he turns left (outbound, away from the field) to a course of 221° and follows the localizer course by keeping the needle centered. He may now descend to 1,900 feet. He then turns right to 266° for one minute, to make the "procedure turn," then left to 086°. This maneuver gets the pilot headed back toward the field with plenty of time to get lined up for his final approach. When the localizer needle again swings toward center, he steers 041°, headed straight for the runway now on the final-approach course. As he nears the OM, still at 1,900 feet, the glide-slope needle swings down to its center position. As he flies over the OM he will hear its signal, see a flashing light on his panel, and his localizer and glide-slope needles will be centered. He is now in the exact position to begin his precision descent. Keeping both ILS needles centered as shown in figure 11.3 will bring him down to an altitude of 455 feet (only 200 feet above the ground!) at the MM, where he will hear another signal. If he can see the runway at this point, he abandons his instruments to land by looking through the windshield. If the weather is so bad that he cannot see the runway, he stays on instruments and executes a "missed approach," climbing back up to a safe altitude to request another approach or a clearance to a different airport where the weather might be better.

Many airplanes, particularly smaller ones, do not have glide-slope receivers, but can still make instrument approaches on an ILS system. Using the localizer to bring them to the end of the runway, they can control their descent with altimeter and clock and fly a safe glide path. But they are not allowed to descend on instruments to as low an altitude as an airplane with full ILS equipment. Many airports do not have ILS systems, but have approach procedures that use omni or ADF stations. The instrument pilot must know how to use them all.

That's a lot of detail to absorb at one sitting, but the way all of this equipment fits together, from takeoff to landing, will be apparent as we make an instrument flight between the two cities.

Since this is to be an imaginary trip, we might as well plan to have fairly good rather than miserable weather. We'll assume that our weather briefing by the FAA Flight Service Station at Memphis has given us the Memphis weather as 2,000-foot

FEDERAL AVIATION AGENCY **FLIGHT PLAN**						*Form Approved.* *Budget Bureau No. 04-R072.3*
			1. TYPE OF FLIGHT PLAN FVFR / VFR X IFR / DVFR			2. AIRCRAFT IDENTIFICATION N8995J
3. AIRCRAFT TYPE/SPECIAL EQUIPMENT [1] PIPER PA-28	4. TRUE AIRSPEED 120 KNOTS	5. POINT OF DEPARTURE Mem. Int'l.	6. DEPARTURE TIME PROPOSED (Z): 14:00	ACTUAL (Z)		7. INITIAL CRUISING ALTITUDE 6000
8. ROUTE OF FLIGHT V54						
9. DESTINATION (Name of airport and city) Adams, Little Rock		10. REMARKS —				
11. ESTIMATED TIME EN ROUTE HOURS: 1 MINUTES: 0	12. FUEL ON BOARD HOURS: 5 MINUTES: 0	13. ALTERNATE AIRPORT(S) —		14. PILOT'S NAME N.F. Smith		
15. PILOT'S ADDRESS AND TELEPHONE NO. OR AIRCRAFT HOME BASE Skyranch Airport, Houston Texas	16. NO. OF PERSONS ABOARD 2	17. COLOR OF AIRCRAFT White & Red		18. FLIGHT WATCH STATIONS —		
CLOSE FLIGHT PLAN UPON ARRIVAL		[1] SPECIAL EQUIPMENT SUFFIX A — DME & 4096 Code transponder B — DME & 64 Code transponder D — DME		L — DME & transponder—no T — 64 Code transponder U — 4096 Code transponder X — Transponder—no code		

FAA Form 7233—1 (4-66) FORMERLY FAA 398 0052-0

11.4 IFR flight plan

COURTESY OF FEDERAL AVIATION AGENCY

broken ceiling (clouds 2,000 feet above the ground level, covering 6/10 to 9/10 of the sky), 10-mile visibility, a northeast wind of 8 knots, and cloud tops at 4,000 feet. Little Rock has a 800-foot overcast with occasional light rain and 5-mile visibility. Both conditions are forecast to continue through the morning. With this weather, we could leave Memphis without an instrument flight plan and legally fly below the clouds. But the ceiling at Little Rock is too low for VFR — we could not fly there unless we were on an instrument flight plan.

Our flight plan (figure 11.4) is filed with the FAA Flight

Service Station, requesting airway Victor 54 and an altitude of 6,000 feet. With our preflight checkout complete, we climb aboard and start the engine. Radios are turned on, and tuned to ground control.

"Memphis Ground Control, this is Cherokee 8995 Juliet on the ramp, IFR to Little Rock, taxi instructions please."

"Cherokee 95 Juliet, Memphis Ground. Taxi to runway nine, hold short. I'll have your clearance for you there."

"95 Juliet." We acknowledge this sort of instruction with just our number or by clicking the microphone button. Most instructions during instrument flight we will be required to repeat or "read back" so that the controller can be sure we heard him correctly.

While we are taxiing out to runway 9, we check the operation of our instruments, particularly the directional gyro and the turn indicator. Near the end of runway 9 we "hold short" by stopping on the taxiway well clear of the runway, run through the takeoff check list, and set up our radios for departure. One omni receiver is set on Memphis VOR (115.5), with the course selector set on 257°, our course for airway Victor 54.

"Cherokee 95 Juliet, this is Memphis Ground Control. I have your clearance."

"This is 95 Juliet, go ahead."

"ATC clears Cherokee November 8995 Juliet to the Adams airport via vectors to Victor 54, flight-plan route, maintain 4,000."

Having copied the clearance on our pad, we read it back to him:

"Okay, understand Cherokee 95 Juliet is cleared to Adams via vectors, Victor 54, flight-plan route, maintain 4,000."

"Readback is correct, 95 Juliet. Contact tower when ready."

After one last check of our instrument panel and our charts, we dial tower frequency.

"Memphis Tower, Cherokee 95 Juliet ready for takeoff, IFR Little Rock."

"Cherokee 95 Juliet, cleared for takeoff. Maintain runway heading."

"95 Juliet is rolling."

We taxi into position on the runway and open the throttle. When the airplane lifts off we hold compass heading 090°, the heading for runway 9,* and begin our climb to 4,000 feet. We keep a sharp lookout for other airplanes. We are in VFR conditions, and other airplanes may be around.

"Cherokee 95 Juliet, contact departure control 119.1."

"95 Juliet switching to departure control."

The transmitter is tuned to the new frequency.

"Cherokee 8995 Juliet is on departure control."

"Cherokee 95 Juliet, this is departure control, radar contact. Turn left to heading 270. Report reaching 4,000."

"95 Juliet to 270 — will report 4,000."

Now departure control has us on his radarscope, and has turned us west (compass heading 270°) in an established departure pattern toward our airway.

At 2,000 feet we slip into the clouds. Now we are in reserved airspace, and we concentrate on our instruments. Turbulence tosses the airplane around a bit and keeps us busy as we climb toward our assigned altitude. At 4,000 feet we level off, still in the clouds. It is very bright above, so the top cannot be far away.

"95 Juliet is level 4,000."

** Airport runways are always numbered according to their compass bearing, with the last zero dropped. A runway with a bearing of 90° is runway 9.*

"Roger, 95 Juliet, climb and maintain 6,000."

"95 Juliet leaving four for six."

Six thousand feet was the altitude we had requested in the flight plan, and the controller gave it to us as soon as his other traffic permitted. In a few moments we break out of the clouds into the bright sunshine. How different it is from the gloomy conditions below! The sky is dark blue above, and the clouds below are a sea of white, dazzling and beautiful. The air is smooth now as we continue to climb to 6,000 feet. Again we must be on the watch for other airplanes. This is VFR airspace again, and not ours exclusively.

"Cherokee 95 Juliet, turn left to heading 240 to intersect Victor 54, maintain own navigation."

The controller has now aimed us at the airway and has told us to find and follow it on our own. Just for fun we tune the ADF to the Bruins radio beacon and find that the ADF needle points straight ahead. We know now that we will intersect airway V54 near Porter intersection (figure 11.1).

We can relax a bit now and enjoy the brilliant day which we climbed into a few minutes ago. Under the bright sun the air is cool and comfortable. The earth has disappeared; the rolling drifts of clouds below stretch as far as we can see in all directions (figure 11.5). A vapor trail from a jet airplane marks the blue dome overhead to remind us that we are not quite alone. In spite of the roar of our engine, it seems a quiet, empty, restful place. None of the hustle and bustle of the world below — no traffic lights, no speed limits, no billboards, no litter, no other drivers. Just us, suspended here in our wonderful flying machine with its clever dials and black boxes.

Our omni needle swings slowly toward center to tell us that we are intersecting the airway. As we turn to a compass head-

11.5 An airplane on an instrument flight plan can fly in the smooth clear air above the weather. COURTESY OF PIPER AIRCRAFT CORPORATION

ing of 257° to follow the invisible highway, we find that the controller is watching us on his radarscope.

"Cherokee 95 Juliet, your position is twenty-three miles from Memphis VOR at Porter intersection. Contact Memphis Center now on 127.2."

"95 Juliet to the center. So long."

We switch to center frequency.

"Memphis Center, Cherokee 8995 Juliet with you at 6,000."

"Cherokee 95 Juliet, Memphis Center, radar contact."

He has been watching the little spot of light on his scope that is us, and will be doing so all the way to Little Rock.

We note that our omni needle moves slowly to the right, indicating that the wind is drifting us to the left of course. We turn right ten degrees and the needle slowly moves back toward the center again as we approach the center of the airway. The ten-degree correction would carry us across the airway to the right, so we reduce it to five degrees and find that this seems to be about the right heading to follow the airway.

"Cherokee 8995 Juliet, traffic at ten o'clock, northbound eight miles, and one o'clock eastbound six miles, both slow-moving."

The center knows our altitude, and may not tell us about other airplanes under his control that he knows won't bother us. But he also sees other traffic that is not under his control. Because he doesn't know its altitude, he doesn't know whether the airplane is a hazard to us or not, so he tells us about it.

"95 Juliet, no contact."

We tell him that we don't see the traffic, but we're looking. The "ten o'clock" tells us to look a little ahead of our left wing, while the "one o'clock" is just to the right of our nose. Twelve o'clock would be straight ahead.

"95 Juliet, traffic now nine o'clock, one mile."

We look to the left and see an airplane approaching several thousand feet above our level, and no problem for us.

"95 Juliet, we see him."

As we reach the halfway point on our flight, we switch to Little Rock VOR, and reset our course selector to 255° (075 + 180) to follow the airway to our destination.

"Cherokee 8995 Juliet, Memphis Center. Contact Little Rock

Approach Control on 124.2 at Hazen intersection."

Now we have to find HAZEN, an imaginary point somewhere in the air ahead of us (figure 11.1). We are on the airway, so we need only to set up the second omni receiver to tell us when we get to Hazen. We dial the frequency of Pine Bluff VOR (116.0) and set the bearing selector to 022°. When we cross the 022 line, on the airway, both omni needles will be centered, and we can announce:

"Little Rock Approach Control, Cherokee 8995 Juliet, Hazen intersection."

"Roger, 95 Juliet, report Tower intersection for radar identification."

Now he knows where we are, but he can't quite see us or identify us for certain on his radar as yet. With the Pine Bluff omni bearing selector reset to 360°, the needle swings to the center in about six minutes.

"Cherokee 8995 Juliet showing Tower intersection."

"Cherokee 95 Juliet, turn left to heading 240 for radar identification."

He wants to be sure that's us he's looking at on his scope. We are now off the airway and under his control entirely.

"Cherokee 95 Juliet, radar contact. Continue present heading for radar vectors to final approach course, runway four. Descend and maintain 4,000." We now know that he will aim us at the outer marker and expect us to fly the approach straight in, without the "procedure turn" we would use if we had no radar guidance.

"Cherokee 95 Juliet is leaving six for 4,000." We now set the Adams ILS localizer and glide-slope frequencies into our receivers, tune the Little Rock radio beacon with the ADF, and turn on the marker-beacon receiver. We level off at 4,000 just skimming the tops of the clouds. We haven't seen the ground in over 100 miles, but we know just where we are and have everything set up to find the end of the runway. We look over the approach plate (figure 11.2) and our landing checklist and get ready for another descent.

"Cherokee 95 Juliet, turn right to heading 260, descend and maintain 2,000."

"95 Juliet turning right to 260, out of four for two." We are south of the airport now, the ADF needle says that the OM is off to our right. We descend into solid clouds, completely on our instruments. Before we reach 2,000 feet approach control aims us at the outer marker.

"Cherokee 95 Juliet, four miles south of the outer marker, turn right to heading 020, cleared for ILS approach to runway four. Call Adams Tower 118.7 at the outer marker."

"95 Juliet to 020, understand cleared for an approach." We continue our descent now to 1,900 feet, as specified by the approach plate, and soon the ILS needles begin to move toward the center. We swing right to the ILS compass heading of 041° and things begin to happen. The OM light on the panel blinks, the signal "beeps" on our loud speaker, and the ADF needle swings to point "behind" instead of "ahead." We don't need all three indications, but it is reassuring to have all of them tell us that we have passed the outer marker.

"Adams Tower, Cherokee 8995 Juliet, outer marker inbound."

"Cherokee 95 Juliet, continue approach. Let me know when you have the field in sight."

This is the most demanding phase of instrument flying. We must scan our instruments rapidly, controlling course, rate of descent, and speed very accurately while keeping the two ILS needles centered. We begin to see glimpses of the ground below but stay glued to our instruments. 1,200, 1,100, 1,000 feet — and we're suddenly out of the clouds with the runway glistening wet ahead of us, right where our instruments said it would be.

"95 Juliet has the runway in sight."

"Roger, 95 Juliet, cleared to land, runway four."

After touchdown, the tower turns us over to ground control.

"Cherokee 95 Juliet, turn off next taxiway, contact ground control, 121.9."

"Ground control, 95 Juliet to the ramp."

"95 Juliet is cleared to the ramp."

The wet gloom down here makes us wish that we could have stayed up above. Two small miracles have been performed for us by our instruments and the great Air Traffic Control system. A flight that would have been impossible not many years ago has been completed safely and pleasantly. And in the bright, beautiful world above the clouds we have enjoyed one more hour of sunshine than people on the ground will have today.

12

Beyond the Speed of Sound

STREAKING ACROSS THE SKY at supersonic speeds, research airplanes and military aircraft regularly fly through what was once believed to be an impenetrable barrier: the speed of sound. Although not really a barrier at all, the speed of sound was for a time a great puzzle to the aeronautical world, and one of the most difficult obstacles it ever faced.

As airplane designers and manufacturers rapidly pushed speeds of military airplanes higher and higher prior to World War II, they were quite unaware that there might be trouble ahead. Then the first signs appeared in the laboratory — tiny ripples in the air on wing models in very high-speed wind tunnels. The ripples looked like the small distortions we see when looking through a piece of glass that has internal defects, or a pane of glass that is streaked by a few drops of rain. Some engineers refused at first to believe that these ripples or streaks were real. Perhaps they *were* merely flaws in the wind-tunnel windows, or perhaps the camera was playing tricks.

But the streaks, whatever they were, seemed to have violent effects on the air flow over the models. New experiments showed that the streaks were *shock waves,* and quite real. Before long a series of military air disasters showed that the mysterious new shock waves were more than just a scientific curiosity. The heaviest, most powerful military fighter airplanes, the pride of America's air defense, began plunging earthward from high altitudes in uncontrollable dives. Pilots who managed to escape crashing were unable to explain the cause of their wild ride straight down. They knew only that they were traveling at a very great speed at a high altitude, usually in a more or less shallow dive, when some unseen force suddenly struck. In spite of the pilot's efforts to resist, the unknown force seemed to take over and lock the airplane in a bucking, screaming dive toward the earth. Both airplane and pilot often were destroyed.

As is the case with many discoveries, after the shock waves had been recognized, engineers could see that they should have expected them all along. Boats moving on the surface of the water show us shock waves that look like those found in subsonic, sonic, and supersonic flight. A slow-moving canoe or rowboat makes only small ripples that move off in all directions and disappear. This is the "subsonic" case, in which the boat is moving more slowly than the wave disturbances it creates.

A rapidly moving tugboat raises ahead of its bow a huge wave of water that extends a great distance from the boat. This is the condition at or near the speed of sound — the "sonic" case — where the boat is moving at about the speed of wave motion.

A speed boat "planing" across the water creates a small wave, or perhaps several waves, that extend straight back at an angle like the sides of the letter *V*. This is the "supersonic" condition where the boat is moving faster than the speed of wave motion.

We can examine these waves in more detail in a bathtub, a large pan of water, or even a large puddle. If you hold a pencil or a small stick perpendicular to the water, with its tip submerged, and vibrate it gently but rapidly, you will see small waves that move away from the stick in all directions in a circular pattern (figure 12.1a). These waves are in some ways sim-

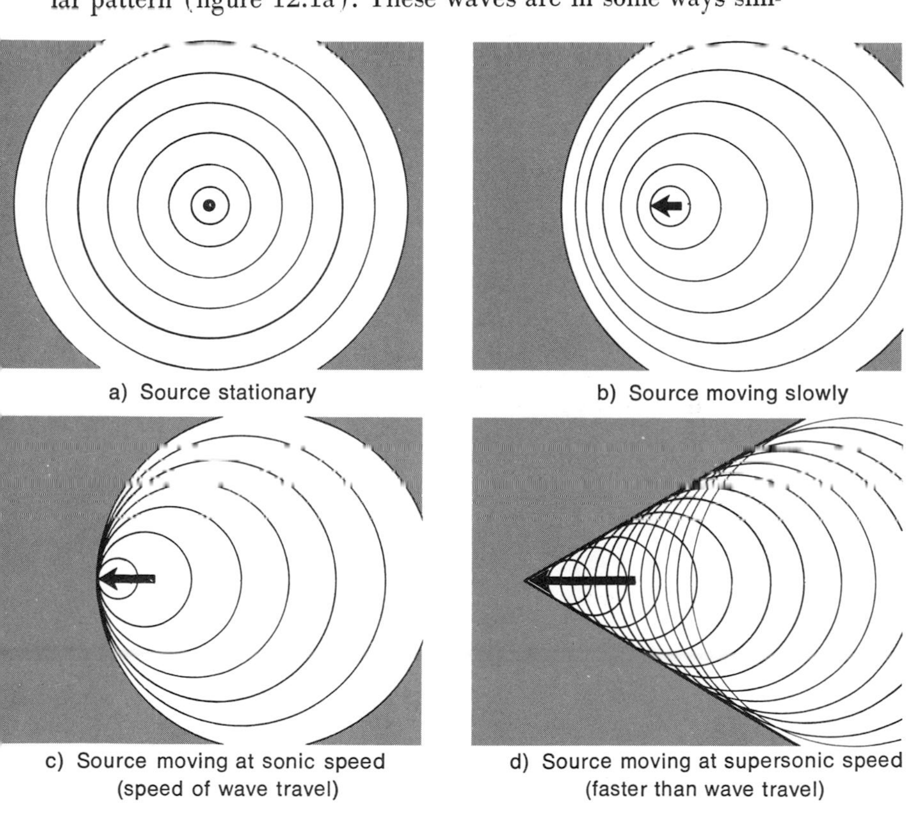

12.1 Wave motion and shock waves

ilar to sound waves in air. Sound waves travel very fast in air — about 1,100 feet per second (760 miles per hour) — but waves on the surface of water travel very slowly and can be readily observed and studied.

If you now move the vibrating stick through the water slowly, at a speed less than the speed of wave travel, the circular wave pattern changes as it moves with the stick (figure 12.1b). The waves are spaced closer together ahead of the source (the vibrating stick) and farther apart behind the source, but the waves still move away and "escape" in all directions. This experiment corresponds to *subsonic flight* in which the airplane is traveling more slowly than sound waves travel in the same air. Because the sound and disturbance waves of a subsonic airplane can move ahead of the airplane, you can hear the sound of the airplane as it approaches.

If you move the stick through the water with a speed about equal to the speed of wave travel, you will see a new pattern. The waves will spread still farther apart behind the source, but will no longer spread out and move ahead of it. Instead, they pile up in a single large wave that moves steadily along just ahead of the source (figure 12.1c). This pattern corresponds to *sonic flight*, or to the condition where the speed of the airplane (or the speed of the airflow over the airplane at a particular point) is just equal to the speed of sound-wave travel. The disturbance waves, though they may have been tiny and unimportant individually at lower speed, now cannot escape but instead pile up ahead to make a "shock wave" of great strength. We'll return to the effects of these shock waves in a moment.

Back to the puddle or the bathtub once more, to move the stick at a speed *greater* than the speed of wave travel. (You needn't vibrate the stick this time — just zip it through the water.) Now an entirely new kind of flow pattern appears (figure 12.1d). The wave front — or shock wave — now sweeps back in a V-shaped pattern behind the stick. All of the disturbance waves produced by the stick are now located within this triangular area behind the shock wave. These disturbances have created the shock wave, of course, by piling up along the swept-back line. The angle of this shock depends upon the speed at which the disturbance travels: the higher the speed, the more the shock is swept backward. This condition corresponds to *supersonic flight,* where the airplane is traveling faster than the speed at which its disturbance waves can travel. The fluid ahead of the disturbance has no advance notice that something is coming. If you were standing on the ground below the path of an airplane traveling at supersonic speed, you could not hear it until the shock wave had passed and you were "inside" the wedge of disturbances it leaves behind. The airplane is literally running ahead of the noise and disturbance it is making!

We can see from this experiment that the speed of wave travel in a fluid has a great deal to do with how the fluid reacts to a vehicle traveling through it. The speed of wave travel in air is the speed of sound. We might expect, based upon our puddle analogy, that the airflow over an airplane might change drastically as the airplane approaches and exceeds this speed. Engineers find it useful to express airplane speed as a decimal fraction of the speed of sound, that is, airplane speed divided by the speed of sound. This term is known as the *Mach number* (M).

$$M = \frac{\text{Speed of the aircraft}}{\text{Speed of sound in same air}}$$

The speed of sound is not always the same, but changes with the temperature of the air. Because air temperature decreases as altitude increases, the speed of sound at high altitudes is less than at sea level:

Altitude (ft)	*Speed of Sound* (mph)
0 (sea level)	760
10,000	735
20,000	708
30,000	680
40,000	665

An airplane traveling at 380 miles per hour at sea level, for example, would move at a Mach number of:

$$M = \frac{380}{760} = 0.50$$

Getting back to the matter of shock waves on airplanes, it is important to note that the airplane need not fly at, or even close to, the speed of sound ($M = 1$) in order to encounter shock waves. In Chapter 3 we learned that at many points on the airplane — over the top surface of the wing, for example — air speeds are always greater than the forward speed of the airplane. On an airplane designed for subsonic flight, local airspeeds might reach the speed of sound while the airplane itself is traveling at only two-thirds the speed of sound ($M = 0.66$) or less.

Research engineers needed a closer look at the shock waves

and the airflow around them. Pressure waves, because they change air density, can refract (bend) light waves like flaws in glass, and can be seen under some conditions with the naked eye, as mentioned earlier. The air over a highway or patch of desert seems to shimmer and dance on a hot sunny day because the rising currents of heated air refract the light passing through them. By means of special optical technique known as *schlieren photography*, waves in air, such as shock waves, can be made to stand out in sharp blacks and whites.

With photographs like those shown in figure 12.2, researchers could study their mysterious adversaries, the shock waves. The dark shape in each picture is an endwise view of a high-speed airfoil. The white streaks or lines are shock waves. The smooth flow at the lowest speed (Mach number = 0.4) is quite different from the violent conditions we see at the two highest speeds, where the flow literally tears away from the wing surface behind the strong shocks. Because it has lost some of its ability to deflect air downward, the airfoil loses lift. This condition is sometimes called *shock stall*. High-speed schlieren motion pictures showed the shock waves were not at all steady but flopped back and forth wildly, pounding the wing with sudden changes in lift. We can see that the rough flow at these speeds must be avoided, for neither the airplane nor the crew could be expected to withstand such a pounding.

The rough ride was thus explained, but what about the sudden vertical dive? As we learned in an earlier chapter, the airplane is a bundle of air deflectors, with each surface doing its delicate job of providing balance and control. If the flow over any surface changes drastically, we can expect trouble. Suspicious of the shock stall and its sudden destruction of wing lift, engineers looked hard at the wing flow. They were

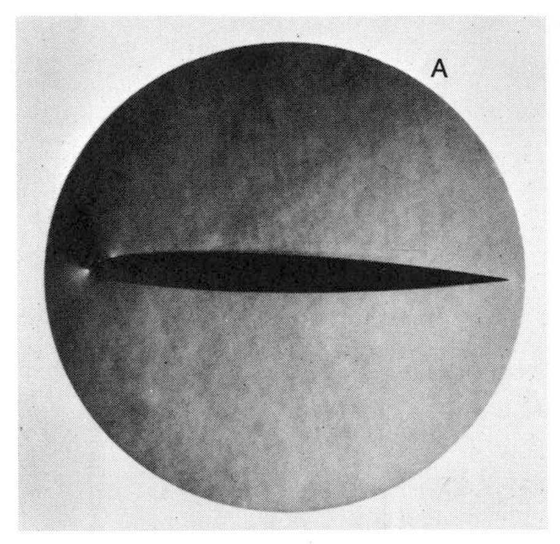

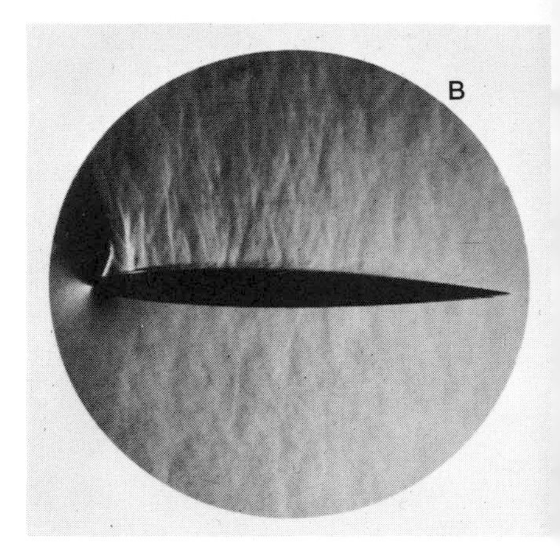

A No important disturbances at this speed. The bright point at the leading edge is the "stagnation point" at which the air divides to pass over and under the airfoil   M = 0.4

B Weak pressure disturbances drift forward over the top surface and pile up as small shock waves (heavy bright lines) near the nose   M = 0.65

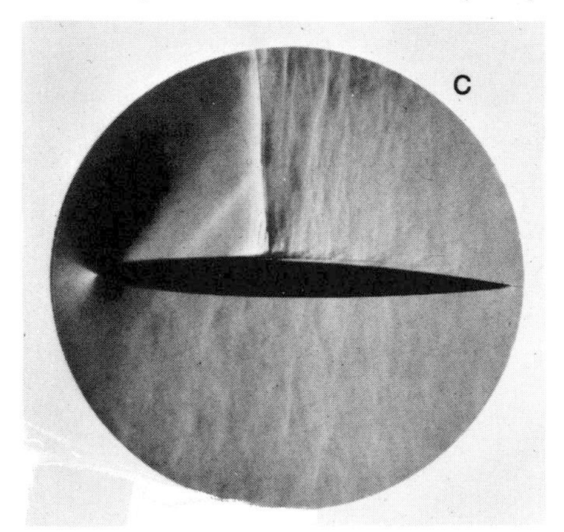

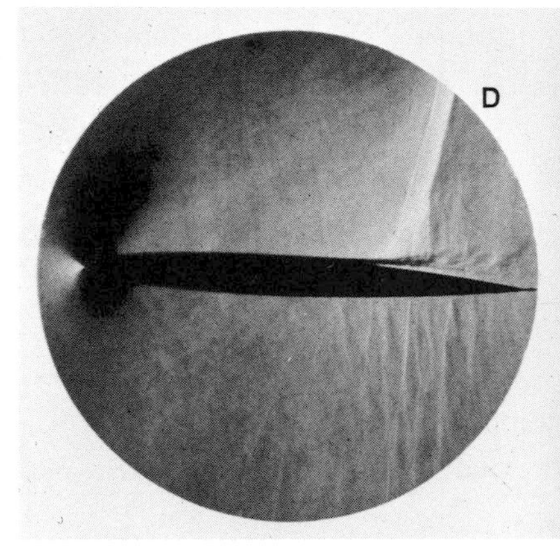

C The shock wave is now strong and has moved back. The flow is separated from the surface of the airfoil behind the shock wave   M = 0.75

D The strong shock wave is badly separating the flow, reducing the lift of the airfoil   M = 0.83

12.2 Special optical techniques make shock waves visible in these schlieren photographs of airflow over a wind-tunnel model.

looking in the wrong place. Shock stall on the wing was the culprit, but it had an accomplice — the horizontal stabilizer.

The sketches in figure 12.3 show what was happening. For normal flight conditions, the wing turns the air downward (upper sketch), and the horizontal stabilizer is mounted at an angle that aligns it with this downflow. When shock stall begins to destroy the lift on the wing, the downflow behind the wing is suddenly decreased. Instead of sweeping downward over the stabilizer (center sketch), the air strikes it from underneath. The upward force on the stabilizer wrenches the airplane over into a dive.

As the airplane picks up more speed, the havoc of the shock waves increases. More wing lift is lost, and the dive steepens. The huge air forces are too large for the pilot to overcome with his elevator control, and in a matter of seconds the airplane is pointed straight for the ground.

We can imagine the pilot's desperate feeling — suddenly finding himself locked in a screaming near-vertical dive, traveling too fast to bail out, and quite unable to budge the control stick of his roaring, bucking airplane. But if he can sit there patiently enough, he may yet escape. The airplane will speed up only until its drag is equal to its weight. Then it will begin to slow down again as its drag increases in the thicker air at low altitudes. Also, the speed of sound is increasing closer to the ground, so the airplane's Mach number is decreasing. The pilot who keeps tugging on the stick, though it feels hopeless, may suddenly find himself pulling out of the dive. The airplane has slowed to where the shock waves have weakened or disappeared, lift has returned on the wing, and the airplane is controllable once more. Some pilots pulled out too suddenly and ripped the wings off their airplanes. Others simply crashed into

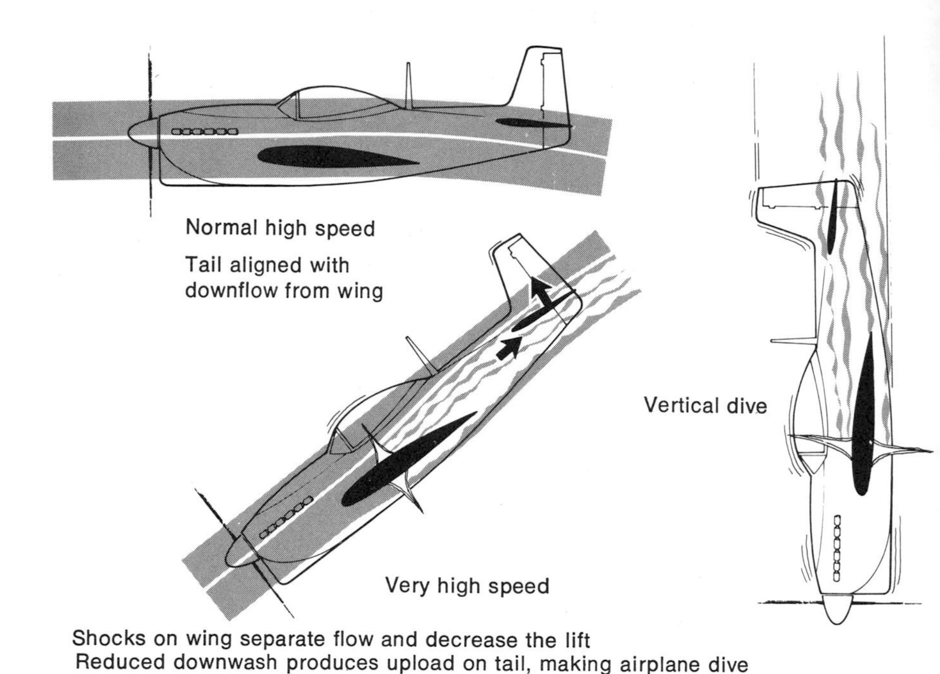

12.3 Shock waves destroy the lift on the wing of a subsonic airplane and push it into a vertical dive.

the ground, head on, at terminal velocity. One pilot had the bright idea during his wild dive of lowering the landing gear. Somehow the gear was not torn off by the slipstream, but slowed his speed to where he could safely pull out of the dive.

As soon as the reason for the crashes was understood, airplanes that were likely to get into this kind of trouble were restricted against diving while flying at high speeds and high altitudes. Pilots were briefed on what might happen and what they should do in case they got into this situation accidentally. Some airplanes were equipped with a small, sturdy flap below the wing. A pilot in trouble could extend this flap to make the wing deflect more air downward, in spite of the shock waves, and thereby restore some lift to the wing. The downflow over the tail was also restored, and the airplane could be pulled out of its dive.

Although the propeller-driven fighter airplanes of World War II could get into pretty desperate trouble with shock waves, or "compressibility," as it was called, at high speeds, they could never attain the speed of sound — not even in a full-power, vertical dive. With their thick, blunt wings and subsonic streamlining, they produced an enormous disturbance at very high speeds. Some three or four times the power of their engines would be required to propel them at sonic speed. To make matters worse, shock waves on the propeller blades began to rob the airplane of thrust above about 400 miles per hour, even in level flight. Although these fast fighters were the most powerful airplanes for their size ever built, they had no chance of achieving supersonic speeds. The aviation world began to believe that supersonic speeds, which had long ago been reached by gun-fired bullets and projectiles, would never be achieved by airplanes.

The terms "sound barrier" and "sonic wall" were invented, and people began to think that a real wall — of air or whatnot — was preventing flight beyond the speed of sound. There is no wall, of course, and there never was — not even a wall of air. There is only a speed region where mixed subsonic and supersonic airspeeds on the airplane's surfaces produce shock waves with violently rough airflow and extremely high drag.

If airplanes were to smash through this region to fly at supersonic speeds along with bullets and projectiles, engineers had to learn what airflows at sonic and supersonic speeds are like, then design the surfaces and controls of the airplane to accommodate them. Their problem was made more difficult by the fact that flight tests at these speeds were either dangerous or impossible with existing airplanes. Research in wind tunnels was difficult, too, because shock waves choked up the tunnel airstream right at the most important speed, the speed of sound.

But the research teams that industry and government had put together during World War II answered the challenge. With special wind tunnels, rocket-powered models, and improvised methods they probed the mysteries of the sonic region to learn its secrets. They began to believe that a properly designed airplane with enough thrust could fly through this region, and that above the speed of sound, flight would once more be smooth. Supersonic shock waves (figure 12.4) would attach themselves to leading edges and other points on the airplane, but like the swept-back wake of a planing speedboat, the waves would be small and steady and predictable.

How could their ideas be proved? Eventually the sonic region must be explored with an airplane, but how could this be done safely? The answer was a tiny, rocket-powered machine called X-1, the first of a series of special airplanes whose sole purpose was research (figure 12.5). The designers built into the X-1 their best information on how an airplane should be shaped to fly at supersonic speeds. Some of the features are not hard to guess: a thin, sharp-nosed airfoil shape to cause less disturbance and less piling up of shock waves; short, stubby wings instead of long ones; an all-moving horizontal stabilizer–elevator instead of the fixed stabilizer that pitched subsonic airplanes down into hopeless vertical dives. A sharp fuselage nose and careful streamlining everywhere were essential. A thin, slender fuselage would have been the designers' choice,

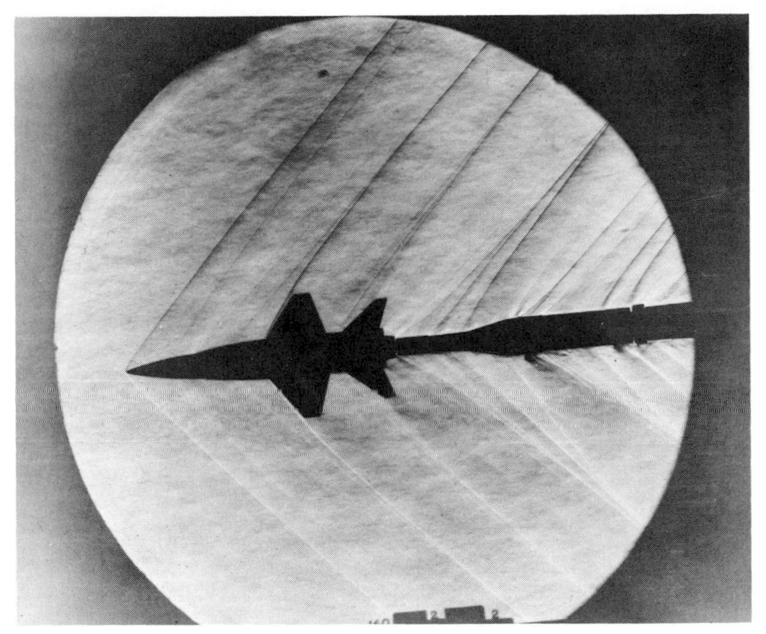

12.4 The supersonic shock waves are steady and the flow smooth on this wind-tunnel model of the X-15 research airplane.

COURTESY OF NASA

but a rather fat barrel-shape was necessary to carry the needed fuel. Because it was headed into an unexplored region of flight, the X-1 was given extra strength everywhere.

The most difficult problem was providing enough thrust to slam the X-1 through the sonic range. Because turbojet engines with enough power were not yet available, the designers looked hopefully toward a liquid-fuel rocket engine. But such an engine would have a tremendous thirst for fuel, emptying the airplane's fuel tanks in only a few minutes. If the airplane took off and climbed to altitude under its own power, it would have no fuel left for the speed run.

So the X-1 was designed to be carried aloft under the belly of another airplane, a four-engine B-29 bomber. After release

12.5 The X-1 airplane

COURTESY OF NASA

at high altitude, the pilot would start the rocket engine and expend all of his fuel in doing what the X-1 was designed to do — explore the sonic and supersonic regions of flight. When its fuel was exhausted, the airplane would glide without power to a landing on the desert seven miles below.

After some preliminary low-speed flights, the X-1 was dropped by the B-29 at 25,000 feet over the California desert on October 14, 1947, for the big attempt at supersonic flight. Captain Charles Yeager rocketed up to 37,000 feet and leveled off for the speed run. Years of research and painstaking effort had gone into this flight. The X-1 did not disappoint the engineers waiting below, although the pilot later admitted being a little disappointed that the feat had been accomplished so easily. The shock waves danced on the X-1 as it approached the speed of sound, but their secrets had been found out, and this time the pilot was firmly in control. The tiny airplane accelerated smoothly to a Mach number of 0.97, then slipped past the speed of sound to a Mach number of 1.05.

The X-1 probed deeper into the supersonic range in over sixty more flights, reaching nearly one and one-half times the speed of sound (957 miles per hour). Its job done, the X-1 was retired in 1950 to a place in the National Air Museum of the Smithsonian Institution beside the Wright airplane and other great aeronautical "firsts." But many perils and many research problems lay ahead. A number of test pilots were killed as faster research airplanes pushed the speed record to twice, then three times the speed of sound.

In the rush for supersonic speeds the subsonic airplane was not forgotten. The new things learned in the sonic region gave designers just what they needed to design a whole new kind of airplane. The new idea of sweepback and thinner wings with special airfoil shapes kept shock waves from forming on wings up to around 600 miles per hour. The jet engine had all the thrust needed to push airplanes up to these speeds at altitudes of 40,000 feet and higher. Military fighters and bombers were soon flashing across the sky at nearly the speed of sound.

The highly successful jet bombers, such as the B-47 and B-52, led to the development of the first jet transport. This airplane, the Boeing 707, and the long line of jet transports that followed, brought a new kind of comfort in air travel to the world. Gone was the noise and vibration of the piston engine. Gone also were many of the weather problems — the jet simply flew above most of the weather. And the speed of 600 miles per hour made even trips across a continent seem short.

Soon turbojet engines with enough thrust for supersonic flight were developed, and military fighters and bombers were built that could fly at supersonic speeds. A new problem sprang up at once. The countryside was rocked by loud explosions that sounded like blasting or cannon fire. The noise was heard as a single "boom" or sometimes as a double "boom-boom," and always struck suddenly and without warning. Sometimes the roar of an airplane could be heard *after* the boom.

The mysterious explosions were soon linked to supersonic aircraft flying overhead. When the airplane passed at very high altitude, the noise was muffled and distant, but when it passed at low altitude, the boom was strong enough to crack plaster and smash large store windows. Complaints of damage and jangled nerves poured in from frightened citizens during the early days of supersonic flight. Farmers even reported nervous cows that refused to give milk and frightened hens that stopped laying eggs.

The loud boom — given names like the "sonic bang" and the "supersonic boom" — was at first thought to be the noise of the airplane "crashing the sound barrier." However, it was soon noticed that the airplane did not make the boom only once as it accelerated through the speed of sound, but rather produced it *continuously* as long as it was flying at supersonic speeds. You've probably already guessed that the supersonic boom is merely the supersonic shock wave.

We see a familiar analogy to the supersonic boom if we stand on a beach watching a speedboat skim by. No disturbance marks the surface of the water at the shore until after the boat has passed. Then the swept-back wave from the boat washes in on the beach, moving along at the same time in the direction of the boat's motion. The water wave that the boat sends to slosh around our ankles is comparable to the shock wave that the supersonic airplane drags along the ground. Because the shock wave is an air-pressure wave, it is felt and heard by our ears as a loud noise.

If we were standing on the ground and a supersonic airplane flew overhead, we would hear nothing until the shock wave swept past. Immediately after the "boom" we would hear the engines and all the other noises of the airplane that trail along in the conical area behind the shock wave (figure 12.6).

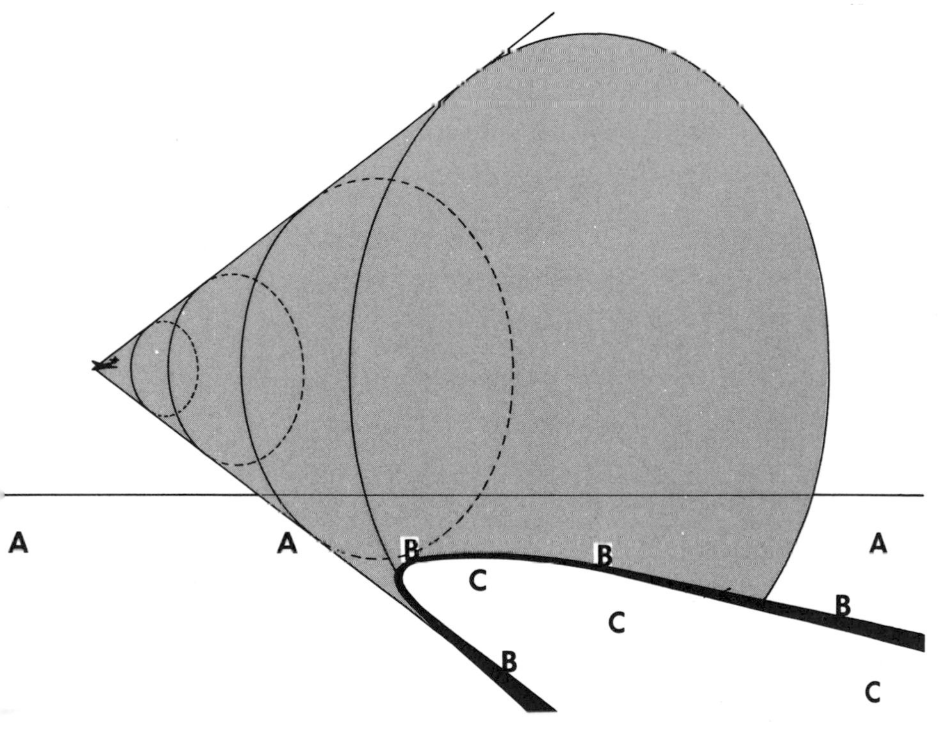

12.6 As the shock wave moves along the ground behind the airplane, a person at A would hear nothing, while a person at B would hear the "supersonic boom" as the shock passes. At any point, C, inside the conical area behind the wave, the noise of the airplane would be heard.

The supersonic boom has not been an important problem because military airplanes are generally flown at supersonic speeds only briefly and at very high altitudes over sparsely populated areas. But plans for a supersonic transport (SST) raised new fears that these large airplanes might blast large areas with supersonic shock waves as they roar across the airways of the world. In addition, there seem to be other possible undesirable effects of the supersonic transports such as engine noise and atmospheric pollution at extreme altitudes. The controversy over this airplane may be the first sign that aviation is nearing a practical limit on speed. Whether or not this is true, another obstacle lies in wait just beyond the speed range of the supersonic transport. This obstacle is a real barrier: heat.

13

The Thermal Barrier, Space, and the Future

THE TEMPERATURE IS sixty-five degrees below zero Fahrenheit in the high, thin air where supersonic airplanes fly, but if an airplane travels fast enough up there, it will glow red hot. The airplane is encountering the *thermal barrier.* Unlike the misnamed "sonic barrier," which was not a barrier at all but only a difficult region to be studied, understood, and flown through, the thermal barrier is a *real* obstacle to high-speed flight in the atmosphere. With clever designs and new materials, engineers may push the barrier to a little higher speed, but they won't get through. It will still be there, hotter and more impenetrable than ever.

Air friction is the cause of the thermal barrier, though the whole phenomenon becomes easier to understand if we look at it from the standpoint of *energy.* If we picture the airplane as standing still while the air flows past it (as in the case of a model mounted in a wind tunnel), we can see that the air has kinetic energy — energy of motion — with respect to the aircraft. As it rubs on the surface of the craft, the air slows down because of friction, and some of its energy is converted into heat. The air closest to the airplane thus becomes warmer and passes its heat to the airplane and to the surrounding air. At a speed of a few hundred miles per hour, the amount of energy in the moving air is small, and the amount of heat it produces is negligible. But at twice the speed of sound, the heat produced may raise the temperature of the airplane's skin to 250° Fahrenheit — hotter than boiling water, and hot enough to begin to rob aluminum of some of its strength. At three times the speed of sound, the temperature of the airplane's skin could shoot up to 600°F — hot enough to melt lead or tin. Because ordinary airplane materials such as aluminum, magnesium, and plastics are useless at this high temperature, an airplane designed for this speed range must be made of special metals such as steel and titanium.

But what about the cargo and crew? Even if the airplane structure and skin can be made to survive 600°, the people, fuel, and a great deal of equipment inside the airplane must be kept cool by some means. If some of the air flowing past the airplane were scooped up to use for cooling, we would find it no help at all. As this air was slowed to a stop inside the airplane, its energy would be converted to heat, making it at least as hot as the air rubbing on the outside skin.

Cooling the inside of the airplane would require refrigeration machinery — a "heat pump" that can pump heat from a cool place (the cabin) to a hot place (the outside air). An ordinary room air-conditioner is a heat pump that removes heat from a 75° room and dumps it into the outside air where the temperature is perhaps 100°. Its job is easy compared to the task of the air-conditioner in the Mach 3 airplane, which must pump heat from a 75° cabin to outside air which has a temperature of 600°! One way to make the problem easier is to chill the airplane's fuel supply before takeoff so it can be used as a place to dump heat from the cabin before the fuel is sent to the engine for burning.

But like all tricks thought up to delay the problem of the thermal barrier, this one pushes the barrier back only a little. At speeds greater than three times the speed of sound, temperatures become so high that ordinary chilled fuel will not soak up all the heat generated during a long flight. Airplanes flying at these speeds might need to use liquid hydrogen for fuel. Besides being an excellent fuel, it has a temperature of —423°F and enormous capacity for absorbing heat.

As might be expected, higher and higher temperatures would make propulsion more and more difficult. Combustion air would become so hot as it slowed in the engine ducts that only a limited amount of fuel could be burned before temperatures too hot for the engine or the ducts to withstand were reached.

For speeds so high that internal propulsion is impossible, a kind of external propulsion has been proposed. Fuel would be sprayed over the rear surface of the wing where it would burst into flame against the red hot surface. The increased pressure produced by combustion would push forward on the wing as a propulsive thrust.

Passengers on such a hypersonic transport would sit in an airplane loaded with liquid hydrogen, looking out the window at wings that were glowing red-hot and wrapped in a sheet of flame. Perhaps the designer who said that hypersonic transports should have no windows has the right idea.

How fast can we fly in the atmosphere? It depends upon how hot we can allow an airplane to become, and upon how much

13.1 The X-15

COURTESY OF NASA

we wish to pay for special materials and construction methods to withstand heat. And that brings us to another question: how *important* is it for us to fly that fast?

If we make an airplane travel fast enough, it will reach a temperature at which any known material will melt. There is no way to penetrate the thermal barrier, and no way around it so long as the airplane flies in the atmosphere. Why not go over the top, outside the atmosphere? If we climb into airless space, we know that there will be no friction and no heating problem regardless of how fast we go. But the escape is only temporary. When the airplane drops back into the atmosphere to land on earth, it will again face scorching heat. Like a spacecraft reentering from orbit, it has a great deal of speed, which represents energy, that will be converted into heat by atmospheric friction.

Having just gotten past the "sonic wall" a few years earlier, engineers were again faced with the problem of how to learn about this new heat barrier and how to test their ideas for dealing with it. The answer was another research airplane, a long, black, stub-winged vehicle named X-15, whose task was to carry a pilot and a load of instruments to hypersonic speeds at the very edge of space. Looking very much like a giant missile (figure 13.1), the X-15 flew, maneuvered, and landed like an airplane. But it was a missile and a spacecraft, too. A rocket engine hurled it toward space, and small reaction jets like those used on spacecraft controlled its attitude in the vacuum of space where its aircraft control surfaces become useless for lack of air to push against.

Like several research airplanes before it, the X-15 was carried aloft by another airplane — a giant B-52 eight-engine bomber. In a typical flight, the X-15 dropped clear of the mother ship about eight miles above the earth and rocketed upward toward the fringes of the atmosphere. Six tons of propellant per minute burned in its rocket engine to produce 57,000 pounds of thrust. When its fuel tanks were empty and the engine had rumbled to a stop, the airplane was traveling at hypersonic speed in a long arcing climb toward space. At the peak altitude the pilot used his reaction-control jets to nose over and hold the correct angle for reentry. Slicing back into the atmosphere at more than five times the speed of sound, the X-15 nose and wings glowed red from the heat of friction. Its surfaces were sheathed in heat-treated Inconel-X nickel-steel alloy, and could withstand temperatures of 1,200°F or more for short periods. As it plunged deeper into the atmosphere, the airplane control surfaces again took hold and the X-15 became an airplane once more.

In nearly a hundred research flights, the X-15 sometimes reached speeds of more than six times the speed of sound (4,100 miles per hour) and altitudes of sixty-seven miles above the earth. This remarkable airplane showed that flight at hypersonic speeds (above $M = 5$) is possible. But temperatures of 2,000°F in a few spots warned of the danger of more speed. Also, the X-15 was designed only for very short flights at these speeds. A longer flight would have sent dangerously high temperatures soaking deep into the innards of the airplane.

The temperatures of the X-15 at the thermal barrier gives us a hint as to why our space crews have not been sent into orbit in airplane-like spacecraft. A spacecraft returning from orbit at 17,000 miles per hour slams into the atmosphere with *more than fifteen times* the energy of the X-15 at its highest speed. Research engineers wondered what would happn to an airplane at these speeds. Wind-tunnel tests of models gave them a flaming answer. The tip of the fuselage and the sharp edges of the wings flashed to a red heat, then simply caught fire and burned like a Fourth of July sparkler (figure 13.2). The energy of the returning craft, whether it is an airplane or a spacecraft, is so huge that it would completely vaporize the vehicle if the energy were allowed to reach it in the form of heat.

This is the "reentry problem," the most difficult part of spaceflight: getting the spacecraft safely back into the atmosphere for landing. How could this be done? This was the problem that had to be solved back in the early days of our space program before the first man could be sent into space.

First of all, aerospace engineers began to see that streamlining was wrong for this kind of flight. Better streamlining, more and more slender shapes, and sharper edges had been the goal through forty years of aeronautical progress. Now the thermal barrier had changed all that. Sharp edges, it seemed, were the first to get into trouble at the heat barrier.

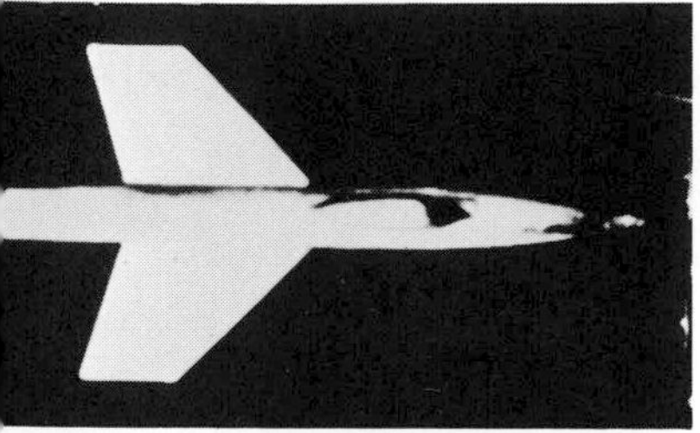

) Model is moved into airstream

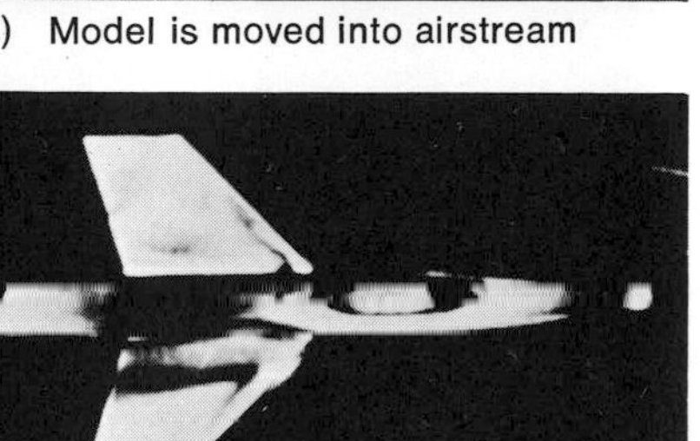

2) Fuselage nose and wing leading edges begin to glow . . .

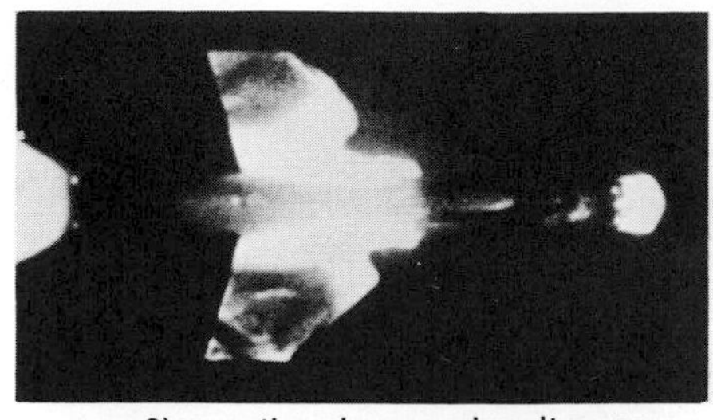

3) . . . then burn and melt away

4) Finally the model disintegrates

13.2 A tiny 2½-inch stainless-steel airplane in research wind tunnel simulates flight at 4,500 miles per hour at 50,000 feet. COURTESY OF NASA

Further work showed that the needed trick was not to *avoid* shock waves, but to produce the most enormous shock wave possible! A broad, blunt forward face piles up a huge shock wave that stands out ahead of the vehicle like the bow wave ahead of a barge. The heat energy released by air compression in this shock wave causes the air to glow white hot. Because the shock wave extends a great distance from the body, most of this heat flows harmlessly past the spacecraft into the atmosphere. The shock wave still bathes the spacecraft in radiant heat that may raise its temperature, to 5,000°F. Fortunately, the enormous drag of the spacecraft slows it so quickly that the period of intense heating lasts for only a few minutes.

The blunt face of the spacecraft can be protected by a thick heat shield and heavy insulation because the blazing shock stands out ahead of the surface. But sharp edges or things sticking out of the spacecraft, such as antennas or wings, would be quickly enfolded by the white-hot shock and simply burned off. For this reason our recoverable spacecraft, including Mercury, Gemini, and Apollo, were designed as simple blunt shapes that are about as far from airplane shapes as one could get. Such shapes could not possibly be made to "fly" when back in the atmosphere, but must be landed by parachute.

But the advantages of being able to fly a spacecraft to an airport for landing would be very great. For one thing, we wouldn't have to land spacecraft in the ocean to be fished out by the Navy; for another, the spacecraft might be used again and again rather than thrown away after only one flight. And a launch vehicle that could be flown back could be reused rather than just dropped into the ocean like the Saturn launching rocket used in the Apollo project.

Designers tried in all three of our manned space projects to make the spacecraft into something flyable by unfolding paraglider wings, rotors, or metal wings, but all were dropped because they were too heavy. Researchers also tried to compromise on shapes that were half blunt body and half airplane. Some of these looked like flying bathtubs — a stubby, well-rounded fuselage with tiny control surfaces sticking outward and upward, not very far, where they might be safe from the shock waves and the heat (figure 13.3). Most of the lift on these vehicles was generated by the body. As we might expect, a stubby body is not a very good deflector of air, and must travel at high speed to generate enough lift to fly. Although these so-called lifting bodies thus had high landing speeds, actual flight tests showed that they could be safely landed like an airplane — or rather like a glider, since there was no engine aboard.

13.3 One of NASA's "lifting body" reentry vehicles
COURTESY OF NASA

More recently other new designs have appeared that seem to be aimed at putting real airplane shapes into space. Huge airplanes they are, with fat fuselages to carry a large amount of rocket fuel (figure 13.4). The wings look very tiny, but they are large enough to land the vehicle when it is nearly

13.4 Space shuttle designs of the future. Model of Saturn V rocket that took Apollo spacecraft to the moon is shown at left for comparison. COURTESY OF NASA

empty of propellant. Huge rocket engines fill the rear of the fuselage for propulsion in space. Turbojet engines may be nestled in the wing for propulsion in the atmosphere while maneuvering for a landing.

The winged spacecraft, known as the "orbiter," is mounted for takeoff on a larger launch vehicle that also looks like an airplane. The "space shuttle," as the two vehicles are called, would take off vertically using the rocket engines of the launch vehicle. When the launch vehicle runs out of fuel, it detaches to drop back into the atmosphere and fly back to the launch site (figure 13.5). The orbiter continues into orbit using its own rocket engine.

When its space mission is completed, the orbiter makes its fiery plunge back into the atmosphere, then glides or flies to the nearest airport for landing. Both vehicles would then be flown back to the launch site to be stacked up on the pad for another trip into space.

The problems of designing an airplane-like vehicle that can survive the blistering heat of reentry are enormous. Temperatures on wing and tail leading edges could soar to 3,000–4,000°F for a short period of time. Special materials such as ceramics would be required, along with heavy heat-shielding and insulation to protect the structure, crew, and cargo inside.

One way in which these high temperatures might be avoided is to forget that the shuttle is an airplane for the first part of reentry and bring it in at a flat angle, belly first, like the blunt face of the old conical shapes. The blazing shock wave would then stand away from the bottom of the airplane, perhaps reducing the need for heat shielding and insulation.

13.5 The shuttle orbiter blasts upward into orbit under its own power while the booster returns to earth. (Artist's conception)
COURTESY OF NASA

In less than seventy years, the airplane has moved from the sand dunes at Kitty Hawk to the edge of space, from 40 miles per hour to 4,000 miles per hour. What lies ahead? How will the airplane affect our lives in the future? Anyone who tries to predict the future of aviation should remember the experience of Professor Simon Newcomb, distinguished mathemetician and astronomer of the last century. Before the invention of the airplane, Newcomb often stated in his lectures and his writing the opinion that man would never fly in a heavier-than-air machine.

After the successful flights of the Wright Brothers, Newcomb was asked whether he felt that passenger-carrying airplanes would ever be built. The aged professor was as sure of himself as ever. No airplane, he reportedly answered, will ever be able to carry more than the pilot.

We know that the speed and comfort of airplane travel have assured the airplane of a permanent and growing place in our world. In the length of time required for an automobile to travel 500 miles, the light airplane can cover 1,500 miles, the jet transport, 6,000 miles. We can expect that more airports, better ground transportation, and airplanes that can land in smaller spaces will increase the advantages and the usefulness of the airplane. Will we travel faster in the future? How fast is fast enough?

The automobile and the light airplane long ago reached a plateau on speed. The speeds of subsonic jet transports have changed little since their introduction in 1957. But intercontinental and global distances are very great, and great savings in travel time are possible with supersonic airplanes. Some people say that progress must always continue, that there will always be a demand for saving time, always an advantage in faster and faster speeds.

But others are beginning to ask new questions about such things as the meaning and importance of "progress" and the need for faster and faster speeds. They are looking also at the effects of man and his machines on the earth's environment, and at the conservation of human and world resources. The supersonic transport, for example, has brought many doubts to the front. A supersonic transport will pour its jet exhaust into our atmosphere nearly twelve miles above the earth, which some scientists think may raise new problems of pollution. It will flood the countryside with a tremendous engine noise during takeoff and climb, and will drag its shock waves along the ground to produce a supersonic boom wherever it goes. Questions are being raised about the huge amount of national and human resources needed to develop such machines, and about the huge amount of fuels required to operate them. The space shuttle is raising similar questions.

Flight at supersonic and hypersonic speeds is possible, but is it desirable? Where does it stand on our list of priorities? How big is our hurry? Where are we going?

Man is beginning to ask questions like these. And the answers will have a great effect not only upon the future of flight, but also upon the future of man himself.

Index